Holistic

Co

Foreword

When I came to Dr. Ward my horses were stressed, we were suffering seemingly endless and recurrent injuries, and everyone had a bad attitude. Like many, I had fallen prey to the allure of "quick fixes" and fads. A friend told me about this "lady veterinarian" who practiced "alternative medicine." It sounded like a fad to me so I could not resist. It was the best decision I have ever made.

Dr. Ward and her program quite literally turned my barrel racing career around. I learned that "quick fixes" are no fixes at all, and that fads are for fashion and not for horsekeeping. Starting with the basics that you will learn in the pages of this book we developed a balanced program of good nutrition, fitness training, general maintenance, and consistency that has enabled my equine partners and me to achieve a level of performance that would otherwise have been beyond reach. Since he's been under Dr. Ward's watchful eye, Risky Chris has won almost every major title in professional barrel racing.

With seemingly infinite patience, Dr. Ward has shown me that there is just no substitute for basic good health. A healthy horse rarely gets stressed, is less prone to injury, and develops a winning attitude. Dr. Ward's program definitely achieves this result.

An exchange with my dad several summers ago pretty much sums it all up. As we were driving to Cheyenne, Wyoming after having won first at the rodeo in Salinas, California, he commented that he couldn't see why I insisted on taking Chris to the "lady chiropractor" every week because it looked to him like Chris was running just fine. I couldn't help but just laugh and tell him that I thought he'd answered his own question.

If you are committed to your horse you will never regret having taken the time to learn about Dr. Ward's program. We are all fortunate that she has taken the time to share with us her vast clinical knowledge and practical experience. The selfish and competitive part of me wishes this book had never been written; the horse lover in me recommends it with unbridled enthusiasm.

Kappy Allen
2000 WPRA World Champion
NFR Average Winner 2000 and 2001
Four Time NFR Qualifier
NFR Record: 40 consecutive clean runs on the same horse

Preface

It is an honor to have the opportunity to share my vision of what makes horses happy and healthy with horse owners like yourself. If you are reading this book, you no doubt are already committed to the holistic care and well being of your horse. More than likely the path you have chosen in horse care has not always been appreciated by your fellow horse owners or horse care providers. You have probably questioned yourself on occasion and wondered if your instincts and motives were sound. The courage to buck the system and stand up for your horse's interests can be a lonely path.

What are you to believe when there is so much information out there? Everyone has an opinion, from your vet to your best friend, about how you are supposed to care for your horse. Books, magazines, websites, and message boards all tout the latest, best things in horse care. The important question is, "What does your horse really want?"

As a holistic equine veterinarian I realize the need for resources through which horse and mule owners can learn about such basic issues as hoof care, equine nutrition and supplements, and general health. I hope this book will offer you the kind of information you need to make informed, empowered decisions for you and your horse.

Madalyn Ward, D.V.M.

Please Note: Throughout this book I will refer to many different techniques, substances, or specific products. Realizing that brand names and products change rapidly through the years, I have tried to keep these references generic in nature. However, where I have found a particular product or brand to be especially efficacious in its effect, you will find sources for ordering or obtaining that product in the appendix.

Acknowledgements

First I would like to thank my many caring, committed clients who refuse to accept anything less than complete health and happiness for their horses. Although challenging at times, working with these clients pushed me to look outside my conventional training to find answers to help their horses. Also, I would like to thank all the wonderful horses who found their way to me and suffered patiently through my attempts to help them. I owe so much gratitude to all of my teachers in both conventional and alternative methods. This book would not be possible without the support and talent of my close friends and editors, Stephanie Yeh and Leta Worthington. I would also like to thank Stephanie's father, Raymond Yeh, for his expert and compassionate business guidance and my personal business coach, Willow Sibert, who helps me stay balanced and focused. Last but not least, I would like to thank God for blessing me with a love for horses and allowing me to spend my life in their company.

SECTION ONE: THE HOLISTIC APPROACH
Chapter 1
Introduction to Holistic Medicine

Palliation, Suppression, and Cure

There is a lot of focus on "alternative," "natural," "herbal," and "holistic" health care these days, for both humans and animals. There are goods and services available in all these areas from a variety of different sources. With so much available, it can be difficult to figure out what is best for your particular horse. It's even confusing to try to figure out what these terms really mean! Although I do use "alternative," "natural," and "herbal" methods in my practice, I've found that using a *holistic* approach produces the best results because it incorporates not only these methods but more, including traditional medicine when necessary.

So what does "holistic medicine" really mean?

~Holistic medicine is an approach which looks at each patient as an individual and focuses on supporting and restoring health.~

A holistic approach considers *anything and everything* that could affect the health of the patient, and works with the patient's own healing forces by either removing blockages or supplying needed substances. Conventional medicine, on the other hand, looks at disease rather than health, and seeks to treat the symptoms of that disease rather than support the patient's own healing force and process.

While some people believe that the difference between conventional and holistic approaches is that conventional medicine uses drugs while a holistic approach uses natural substances, the difference really lies in the basic philosophy of each approach. Conventional medicine focuses on the disease, while holistic medicine considers all aspects that support or detract from a patient's health. With holistic healing, patients usually experience fewer side effects, have less resistance, and are at least as healthy, if not more healthy, after treatment.

What About Symptoms?

Symptoms are the clues that tell us our horses are not healthy and are always the first thing we want to address. Regardless of what therapy or approach is used, there are three basic ways of handling symptoms:

- Palliation
- Suppression
- Cure

As you will see, the following statements demonstrate another fundamental difference between conventional and holistic medicine.

Conventional medicine focuses primarily on palliating or suppressing symptoms—in other words, masking or temporarily alleviating the symptoms without addressing the root cause of those symptoms. When the root cause of symptoms is not addressed, they will appear again and again, often in states that are more and more difficult to palliate or suppress.

Holistic healing, on the other hand, while concerned with symptoms, is focused on actually curing the cause of the symptoms. To a holistic practitioner, symptoms are the body's way of telling us what it needs in order to become balanced and healthy. Please think about this difference for a moment because it is a critical point in understanding the holistic approach.

If we want our animals to be healthy, we have to stop palliating and suppressing symptoms and start curing them! Let's take a closer look at the difference between palliation, suppression, and cure.

Palliating Symptoms

When symptoms are "palliated," you can expect them to disappear temporarily during a course of treatment, but they tend to return immediately or soon after treatment is discontinued. With this approach the disease process itself has not been addressed and continues to advance, often requiring larger doses of medicine to keep symptoms at bay. Giving Bute for arthritis pain is a good example of palliation—the drug eases the pain but doesn't address the root cause of the arthritis. In this example the pain is actually the body's way of telling us something is wrong in the joints. More than likely, the joint fluid has been damaged by an excess of circulating free radicals, which prevents it from properly nourishing the joint cartilage. The cartilage then begins to break down faster than the body can replace it, creating instability in the joint. The body's response to all of this is to deposit calcium around the joint in an effort to stabilize it. This whole process can be slowed or reversed in its early stages, but if symptoms are only palliated the process will continue and permanent damage will eventually occur. Palliation is such a common response to symptoms of disease that you can probably think of many examples yourself.

Suppressing Symptoms

While palliation can eventually result in permanent damage, suppression of symptoms can be even more harmful. When symptoms are "suppressed," they will disappear and will not reappear, but the animal's overall health worsens. This usually occurs with the use of powerful drugs such as corticosteroids, but can also occur when milder drugs are used on a weak animal. For example, a common therapy for treating allergic skin reaction is to give steroids. These drugs will stop the rash but will likely bring about an undesirable change in behavior as well. As a result, your once friendly and willing horse is now aggressive and hateful. This is suppression. The skin rash was a sign of liver imbalance, and when this expression of the imbalance was blocked by steroids the body was forced to express itself at a deeper and more serious level. In this example, besides serious personality changes, the energy of the disease will also eventually manifest again physically, but in another, more serious way than a skin rash. In this case that might typically be actual liver damage.

Curing the Disease

Now you want to hear about CURE! Curing an animal takes time and patience, as the animal's system must be strengthened, obstacles to cure removed, and overall systemic balance restored. This involves an in-depth look at the nutrition, management, and personality of the patient—a comprehensive approach that is not considered in a conventional treatment of symptoms alone. In the arthritic horse, for example, I would give the horse the nutritional support he needed to help the cartilage heal faster. I would also investigate the source of free radicals that were causing damage to the joints. If I found the source to be external, I would remove it and probably add appropriate supplements to the diet to combat the existent free radicals, but if the source were internal, then I would use a healing method such as acupuncture or homeopathy to bring the body back into balance. With cure, not only do symptoms disappear but the vital force comes into full expression. The hair coat shines, the eyes brighten, and the playful spirit returns, even in older animals.

A Review of Palliation, Suppression, and Cure

The vital force of the body produces symptoms in an effort to heal. If symptoms are palliated, they improve as long as the treatment is continued but return when the treatment stops. If symptoms are suppressed, they disappear but the overall condition of the patient worsens. The imbalance or disease continues during both palliation and suppression, so higher dosages or more frequent treatments are needed in order to keep symptoms controlled. To actually *cure* the disease, the patient must be brought back into balance or a state of health where the body no longer needs to produce symptoms. This process involves an in-depth look at the individual and the conditions that brought the patient to a diseased state in the first place.

Holistic Versus Natural or Alternative

"Holistic" is a very broad term that simply means looking at the whole picture. In medicine, the word holistic describes *the way a case is approached*, not the actual treatment used. This is a very important distinction to keep in mind.

For example, if a horse has a fever and cough, and is off his feed, a holistic approach would support the immune system and monitor the patient closely. The rationale would be that the fever, cough, and lack of appetite were symptoms indicating that the body was fighting some form of outside invasion. Whether the invasion was from a virus, bacteria, or toxic insult would not be the most important factor. Supporting the body in general would be the main concern. If the symptoms worsened and it became obvious the horse's immune system was being overwhelmed, then it would *still* be a holistic approach to consider adding support in the form of conventional medicine such as antibiotics, *and/or* natural remedies such as herbs, homeopathic remedies, or acupuncture treatments. Immune support and nursing care would still be continued. Once the horse recovered, holistic thinking would involve improving the nutrition or management program, if needed, in order to build up the horse's resistance. In this example, one might ask questions such as:

1. Was the horse's work schedule too demanding?

2. Could the nutritional status of the horse be improved?

3. Did poor ventilation or excess dust weaken the horse's respiratory system?

4. OR, was your horse simply having a healthy immune response to a pathogen he needed to build immunity to?

The holistic approach to horse care means always asking:

- *WHY* the illness occurred

- *WHAT* the body was attempting to achieve with its response

- *HOW* the body can best be supported

Let's look at another example and see how the holistic approach might be applied. In this case the horse has thin, weak hoof walls. We could ask a set of questions similar to those above:

1. ***WHY?*** Consider, for example, genetics, poor nutrition or digestion, and the environment.

2. ***WHAT*** *does this symptom mean?* If either nutrition or digestion is poor, the body will protect and feed the vital organs first, so thin hoof walls can indicate a shortage of nutrients such as amino acids. Another possibility would be liver stress. The liver, according to Traditional Chinese Medicine (TCM), is connected to hoof health.

3. ***HOW*** *can the body be supported?* Supportive trimming or shoeing might be needed. Better nutrition and digestive aids, liver support and rebalancing, and improved environmental conditions are also possible approaches that should be considered.

Now let's look at some treatment options and whether or not they fit into a holistic approach, irrespective of what medicine or method is used.

An Example of a Natural but Non-Holistic Approach

In our horse with the cough and fever a "natural" approach might be to give the herb echinacea rather than an antibiotic. Echinacea has been proven to have a local antibacterial action on bacteria that secrete hyaluronidase, such as streptococcus. If you suspected your horse was in the early stages of strangles, which is caused by a streptococcus bacterium, then echinacea could be used as a natural antibiotic. This would be an example of choosing a natural course of treatment while still thinking from a Western medicine point of view. In other words, using echinacea addresses the symptoms but not the actual cause of the cough and fever. I am not saying this is wrong, it is just important to understand the difference in the approach. Another natural but non-holistic way to treat our coughing horse would be to use an alternative approach such as acupuncture, but selecting only points to treat fever and cough. A more holistic approach to using acupuncture would be to include points to strengthen the lungs and to correct other possible imbalances. Remember, a holistic approach doesn't just address the symptoms but seeks to understand the cause of the symptoms and address the overall condition or imbalance.

For the horse with thin, weak hoof walls a natural but not necessarily holistic, approach would be to start the horse on a hoof supplement to supply extra nutrients. This might work very well but would not be holistic unless one considered other possible reasons for poor hoof quality and addressed those as well. An alternative treatment such as acupuncture might be used to support the liver, but again, this would not be a holistic approach unless other factors were also being examined and corrected.

In this example, a truly holistic work-up would include determining, if possible, the hoof quality of other horses in the same genetic line. Hoof care would be evaluated to see if the angles were appropriate, and factors in the horse's living environment would also be considered. The horse's overall condition would be examined as an indicator of nutritional status. Other symptoms, such as a dull coat or brittle mane and tail, could indicate poor nutrition or the inability to absorb nutrients. Questions about the personality of the horse or other health conditions, such as allergies, might indicate liver stress. After all this information is gathered, a holistic treatment plan can be started that might include natural nutritional supplements and/or alternative methods such as acupuncture or homeopathy, as well as recommendations for changing the hoof management or trimming methods.

Hopefully you now have a deeper understanding of the difference between conventional and holistic medical models. Conventional medicine focuses on disease and the removal of symptoms. The holistic philosophy focuses on the patient as an individual and considers how to best support the patient's health and remove obstacles that detract from health. Holistic medicine encompasses a broad range of methods and medicines, including drugs. Conventional medicine focuses primarily on drugs and surgery.

Chapter 2
Alternative Healing Modalities

Many different alternative healing methods are now becoming common practice. The term "modality" is commonly used to refer to treatment techniques and will be used frequently in this book. To help you make empowered choices for you and your horse, we will review four of the most popular alternative modalities: homeopathy, acupuncture, chiropractic, and osteopathy.

Introduction to Homeopathy

Homeopathy is a system of medicine based on the principle that "like cures like." In simple terms what that means is that the same thing that can cause a disease can also *cure* that disease. In the early 1800s Samuel Hahnemann, the founder of homeopathy, was the first person to purposely try this approach to treating disease. Hahnemann disagreed with the accepted reasoning behind the effectiveness of the medicine quinine in treating cases of malaria. As an experiment he began to take quinine on a regular basis, and sure enough, after a short time he was actually manifesting the symptoms of malaria in his own healthy body. The symptoms would disappear when he stopped the quinine, only to reappear when he resumed taking it. He concluded that quinine was effective in treating malaria not because of its bitter quality, which had been the previous theory, but because in crude form its energy somehow "matched" the disease and could produce its symptoms.

Hahnemann then began to treat patients according to this principle, using smaller and smaller doses of the substances he was working with. He found his patients not only responded positively, but they also had few of the side effects which were so common to the medications used by more conventional practitioners. He theorized that the homeopathic remedies, in their minute doses, carefully selected to match all of the patient's symptoms, gave the body the information it needed to heal itself. Although no one has been able to prove or disprove this theory, homeopathy is accepted in many parts of the world today as a very scientific method for treating disease.

There are over 1,500 known homeopathic remedies made from animal, vegetable, or mineral sources. Many in their crude form are toxic or inert but when prepared and used according to homeopathic principle they are completely safe and effective.

How to Administer Homeopathic Remedies

Homeopathic remedies are given internally in extremely small doses. Hahnemann discovered that by putting the remedy through a series of dilutions and agitations he was able to make it more potent in action each time. The diluted medicine in this form is thus said to be in a "potency."

A commonly used potency of homeopathic remedies is 30c: the original substance has been diluted by adding one drop to 100 drops of water and agitating; then one drop of this new mixture is diluted in 100 drops of water. This process is repeated 30 times ("30c" therefore refers to 30 dilution processes, each in 100 [c] drops of water). The final solution is infused into small sugar pellets which are taken orally. When giving remedies to horses I usually dissolve four or five pellets in spring or distilled water and squirt it into the horse's mouth with a syringe. Most horses accept this very willingly. The medicine is absorbed by the mucous membranes in the mouth and does not need to be swallowed.

In severe acute conditions the remedies can be given every 15 minutes for up to four doses, or until a response is seen. Less severe acute conditions require less frequent dosage, anywhere from one to 24 hours apart. If four doses of the remedy have not created a response, then it is probably not going to be effective for the condition. If there is a response, the medication is discontinued as soon as the animal is obviously moving toward recovery.

In chronic cases remedies are usually given infrequently and the response to each treatment is carefully monitored. In these cases, extensive histories including current symptoms, previous symptoms, habits, and personality are taken on each patient. The more specific information a homeopathic doctor can acquire about an individual, the more able he is to select the remedy which best matches that information and which will, therefore, probably be the most effective. Follow up calls are done two to four weeks after treatment to evaluate changes that have occurred since the previous prescription. These changes tell the homeopathic practitioner if the remedy is acting well or if additional treatment is needed.

Introduction to Equine Acupuncture

Acupuncture is a system of medicine developed in China over 3,000 years ago. Veterinarians receive their acupuncture training through post-graduate certification courses. While the emphasis in equine acupuncture is often the treatment of the musculoskeletal system, acupuncture can also be used to treat chronic disease. Research has shown that stimulation of acupuncture points causes a systemic reaction in the entire body.

Basic Principles of Equine Acupuncture

In addition to the commonly known systems of the body such as the cardiovascular and nervous systems, the body also has an energy system. Energy, or "Qi" (also often spelled "Chi"), as it is known in Chinese medicine, traverses the body through invisible pathways called meridians. It is these meridians which are regulated by acupuncture points. There are six main pairs of twelve different meridians and two unpaired meridians:

- Lung – Large Intestine
- Heart – Small Intestine
- Pericardium – Triple Heater
- Liver – Gall Bladder
- Spleen – Stomach
- Kidney – Bladder
- Governing Vessel
- Conception Vessel

The Gall Bladder meridian on my horse Frijole.

Acupuncture points are located on meridians, and it is these points that control the flow of energy. Dysfunction occurs when the energy flow is blocked or imbalanced, with one meridian containing too much energy and another too little. Imbalances in the meridians can originate directly from blockages in the meridian itself or indirectly from problems in the related organs. The goal of acupuncture is to remove blockages and balance energy flow throughout the entire body.

Example: The paired Lung and Large Intestine meridians may both be affected in a horse with a respiratory infection. These meridians run down the inside and outside of the front leg, so blockages in these meridians may create a secondary symptom of lameness.

Acupuncture points can be stimulated by several methods including:

- Acupuncture needles
- Aqua puncture—injecting fluid into points
- Acupressure—digital pressure on points
- Electro-acupuncture—electrical stimulation of points
- Moxibustion—use of heat on points
- Cold laser—use of light on points
- Ultrasound
- Gold beads—implanted surgically into points
- Magnets

Example of acupuncture needles in the Bladder meridian.

The use of acupuncture to balance energy in the body is based on the Chinese principle of Yin and Yang. For the body to function at optimum levels it must have a balance of Yin and Yang, or opposite energies, just as the Earth needs a balance of day and night, summer and winter. It is this balance that helps ward off disease. Unlike conventional medicine, Traditional Chinese Medicine does not consider viruses or bacteria as causes of disease. Instead it recognizes that external environmental pathogens or influences invade the body when it is out of balance, thus allowing these organisms to multiply. Examples of such pathogens include:

- Wind
- Cold
- Heat
- Damp
- Dryness
- Fire

These pathogens can invade at the level of the meridians on the surface of the body or deeper in the body to cause serious disease.

Example: Invasion of the Stomach Meridian by Cold would cause stiffness, as Cold causes contraction. Since the Stomach Meridian runs over the stifle joint, stiffness in this area early in a ride before the horse warms up might be the first noticeable symptom, or the "presenting" symptom.

Acupuncture needles above the hoof.

Example: Heat invading the Lungs would present as a fever and a cough with thick yellow discharge. These symptoms suggest a systemic or internal imbalance rather than a localized or external one.

Conditions treated with acupuncture include:

- Lung problems
- Chronic cough
- Allergic bronchitis
- Pneumonia
- Reproductive problems
- Infertility
- Ovarian pain associated with heat cycles
- Scars
- Internal medicine problems
- Organ weaknesses
- Digestive tract problems
- Diarrhea
- Constipation
- Excess gas
- Neck problems
- Pain and stiffness
- Nerve inflammation
- Neurological disorders
- Wobblers
- Nerve damage
- Behavior problems
- Many problems related to pain or energy imbalance
- Chronic pain

- Musculoskeletal disorders
- Navicular
- Arthritis
- Laminitis—acute and chronic
- Tying up (azoturia)
- Colic
- Acute and chronic conditions

Evaluation of Treatment: Poor Response

A poor response to acupuncture may indicate either an incorrect diagnosis or an inappropriate practitioner, and produces:

- Minimal or no improvement after four to eight sessions for small animals and after two to four sessions for large animals

- Results lasting only a few days after each treatment

Evaluation of Treatment: Good Response

A strong positive response to acupuncture produces improvement after four to eight sessions for small animals and after one to four sessions for large animals.

Introduction to Chiropractic

If your horse is not working up to his potential or is stiff and reluctant to move forward, you might want to consider a chiropractic work-up. Back pain, poor performance, or bad attitude could be related to what is called a chiropractic subluxation. The term "subluxation" as a chiropractic term should not be confused with the medical definition. A chiropractic subluxation is the alteration of normal dynamics, anatomical, or physiological relationships of adjacent articular (jointed) structures. The medical definition of subluxation is an incomplete or partial dislocation.

Back pain occurs when chiropractic subluxations cause inflammation around the nerve roots as they exit the spinal cord via the small intervertebral openings. This inflammation initially causes nerves to become hyper-reactive, which leads to muscle spasms because the muscle cells are constantly being signaled to contract. If a subluxation exists for an extended period of time, however, the nerve may be permanently damaged and lose function, and without nerve stimulation the associated muscle will atrophy.

Chiropractic subluxations cause interference with nerve transmission just as turning the dial on a radio causes the signal to fade in and out. If your horse is not getting clear signals through his nervous system, how can he respond appropriately to your signals?

When choosing a chiropractor, it is best to find one that has completed a post-graduate course such as the American Veterinary Chiropractic Association (AVCA) certification course. This course teaches a very safe, low force, high-speed method of adjusting individual vertebral segments. A good practitioner will use speed and skill, rather than force, to make adjustments.

The chiropractic method I use is called network chiropractic. It addresses both type A and type B subluxations. A type A subluxation is usually the result of some physical concussion or other kind of physical stress. For instance, repeated concussion from landing over a jump or repetitive stress on the joints from barrel racing may cause type A subluxations. This kind of physical stress can cause one or more of the vertebrae to become misaligned. When the vertebrae are misaligned, the resulting inflammation and soft tissue swelling can cause pressure on the nerves along the spinal cord and interfere with the transmission of nerve impulses between the nerve cells and tissue.

Network chiropractic does not require much force. (Thank Heavens!)

The second type of subluxation, Type B, involves the spinal-meningeal sheath, which is the membrane that surrounds the brain and spinal cord, and the connective tissue that attaches it to the spinal cord. All of these are associated with the horse's neurological system. Emotional or chemical stress can overload this system, resulting in stress on the spinal cord. The body tries to reduce this stress by moving vertebrae out of alignment. Both Types A and B result in misaligned vertebrae, but the causes are different in each case. Many horses appear to experience emotional stress from training and showing. This type of stress can create meningeal tension which can be addressed by network chiropractic.

The network approach of adjusting uses gentle contacts of a nonspecific nature made in specific areas with the intent to remove tension in the brain and the spinal cord itself. Once the tension has been released, the natural movements of the horse will allow the vertebrae to return to normal position.

Introduction to Osteopathy

Osteopathy derives its name from "osteo," which means bone, and "pathos," which means illness or suffering. Osteopathy, however, encompasses much more than problems with the bones. The fundamental principle of osteopathy is mobility, and the osteopath considers that everything has to move to have proper function. The goal of the osteopathic examination is to evaluate the quality of movement on a local and systemic level, and treatment is designed to return or improve proper motion to an affected area.

The horse has to adapt and defend himself against lifelong internal and external influences, and his only tool is his own vitality. If his vitality is not sufficient to overcome internal influences such as congenital bone or organ anomalies, or external influences such as trauma, microorganisms, drug or environmental toxins, then pathology occurs. Osteopathy is not only concerned with what actually caused the problem but also how the individual animal's vital force responded to the insult. The horse's vitality will respond and react to influences with a variety of systems:

- Musculo-ligamentous system
- Visceral (internal organ) system
- Emotional system

The bones of a horse tell a story, and the osteopath follows this story to determine which areas are affected, eventually deducing the primary cause of the insult to the horse's system. By locating and removing these primary insults, as well as the horse's attempt to cope with them, motion is restored to all parts of the body and vitality can return to its maximum state. For instance, a mare with an inflamed ovary may show tension in her lumbar vertebrae. While a chiropractor will address the tension in the lumbar area, the osteopath will first attempt to relieve the inflammation in the ovary and then address the resulting lumbar tension.

Here I would like to offer an example of a thorough osteopathic examination. First, the osteopath walks around the horse to get a sense of the horse's vitality, posture, conformation, and condition. The horse's gait is briefly evaluated as he is being walked up for examination. The osteopath then starts at the hindquarters by holding the horse's tail and pulling gently back on it. This offers a sense of the tension in the connective tissue of the meningial covering of the spine, which can often indicate a problem with one or more internal organs.

The osteopath again uses the tail to check the position of the sacrum. He then checks the pelvis and each joint in the hind legs for the ability to flex and extend as well as adduct (move toward the midline) or abduct (move away from the midline). He also checks each individual vertebra from the withers and thoracic spine to the lumbar spine. Any area where two or more vertebrae are fixated together tells him that internal organs are involved. Based on which vertebrae are fixated, and because each organ is connected to a specific area of the spine by a network of nerves, the osteopath is able to determine which organs are affected. According to osteopathic theory, 80% of spinal fixations are caused by systemic problems. After very carefully evaluating the spine, the osteopath examines the front legs, cervical (neck) spine, and head in the same manner.

After this full evaluation, only about half the horses are actually given structural adjustments. Many horses are referred for further veterinary tests such as blood work or radiographs. Additional osteopathic procedures may include releasing adhesions from gelding scars or inflammation of the ovaries or uterus. If the osteopath feels the pattern suggests a traumatic accident, he often applies low force adjustments using cranio-sacral principles. For horses with uncomplicated bony fixations, the needed adjustments are done by starting at the hind end and moving forward. Using speed, correct technique and leverage from the horse's own body, the osteopath is able to adjust without excessive force. Horses respond very well to these treatments.

Osteopathy Case Study: Millie

Visual examination of Millie showed a mare who seemed depressed. She had a significant dip in her neck in front of the withers, and her back was roached in the lumbar area (lower back). Hands on evaluation revealed a depressed sacrum, fixation on both sides (bilateral), and all joints in the lower legs turned outwards and unable to rotate in. Her fourth, fifth, and sixth thoracic vertebrae were all fixated to the right, indicating a problem in her lungs or diaphragm. The pulling down of her neck in front of her withers also indicated a problem with her diaphragm. Her pectoral muscles were tender, indicating that she was using those muscles to help her inhale. Both front legs were also rotated outwards and the base of her skull was fixated in extension.

The osteopath in this case believed that all of these findings pointed to a traumatic injury similar to whiplash in a person. This kind of injury occurs when a horse sits back or flips over backward. Craniosacral techniques were used to gently release the diaphragm and meningial tension. The mare appeared greatly relieved and much brighter after her treatment. No structural adjustments were done and an appointment for a recheck was made for a month later to allow her body to release all compensations.

Homeopathy, acupuncture, network chiropractic, and osteopathy are all alternative treatments that work with the energy of the body. With acupuncture, network chiropractic, and osteopathy improvement should be seen in two to four sessions. Excessive force is not needed for effective chiropractic or osteopathic adjustments.

Chapter 3
A Holistic Approach to Nutrition

With so many types of feed, grasses, and supplements available, it can be hard to figure out what you should feed your horse. We all know that good nutrition is important for keeping our horses healthy and happy, but how do we choose among all the different options?

I've come to realize that a holistic approach is just as useful when looking at nutrition as when treating illness. Holistic means looking at the big picture with regard to your horse's health and happiness and determining why things are the way they are. When I first started focusing on nutrition in my practice, I became very frustrated because I didn't approach it from a holistic perspective. I looked up a horse's vitamin, mineral, and protein requirements, and even found the Nutritional Research Council's tables for the ingredients in the feed and supplements I gave my patients. I then tried to make it all fit neatly into a single formula. But, despite all my careful calculations, my patients did not get any healthier.

I finally came full circle several years later when I learned that horses, like all animals, need a wide range of whole food nutrients. Their bodies can then "sort through," absorb, and assimilate what they need, and that may vary from day to day. While this approach seemed less scientific, the evidence I saw in my patients proved that it worked.

There are three main areas of dysfunction where nutrition can help restore and maintain health:

- Lack of quality nutrients

- Failure to absorb and assimilate nutrients

- Free radical damage due to the buildup of metabolic and environmental toxins

What to Feed

The cornerstones of any quality nutritional program are whole foods. Building your program around synthetic nutrients is like building your house out of styrofoam bricks. Everything looks good until there is some kind of stress, and then the whole house comes tumbling down. Because most of the grains we feed our horses are grown with the use of synthetic fertilizers, they do not provide the horse with high quality nutrients. Oats and grass once provided all the nutrition hard-working horses needed, but in this era of poor soil and synthetic soil amendments that is no longer the case.

In addition, during the last 20 years there has been a move away from whole grains to processed pellets. Part of the rationale behind this shift is the lack of nutrients in whole grains. However, producers also realized that pellets can be produced with the cheapest or easiest-to-obtain ingredients available. Problems with pelleted feeds include:

- The added supplements are usually synthetic vitamins and inorganic minerals, which act more like drugs than nutrients in the body. Horses have a more difficult time assimilating inorganic minerals than those derived from natural sources. The body always "recognizes" nutrients in their natural form and knows what to do with them, whereas manmade supplements, even if made from natural ingredients, have to be processed like any other foreign substance. The human body knows exactly what to do with an orange, for example, but has to process a Vitamin C tablet differently in order to sort out what it can and can't use.

- The few remaining natural vitamins in grains or forage products are mostly destroyed during the pelleting process. The smaller and harder the pellet, the more heat was used when it was processed.

- Generic labeling gives very little clue as to what the actual ingredients are (allowing producers to use very poor quality ingredients). Producers might list "grain products" as a main ingredient, which gives them the ability to alter feed formulas at any time, depending on what is cheapest or easiest to obtain. These constant changes make it hard to provide a consistent feeding program.

- Pelleting destroys food enzymes. An enzyme is a specialized protein structure which carries with it an energetic charge. Enzymes speed up chemical reactions that normally take place very slowly or not at all. Foods that have not been heated or processed contain enzymes that speed up their digestion after they are eaten. These same enzymes will cause foods to spoil more rapidly which is why processed foods tend to keep longer. Destroying natural food enzymes by processing extends a product's shelf life, but these foods will require the body to produce extra enzymes to digest them. The enzymes required to digest these foods may deplete the enzymes that would normally be used to complete other chemical reactions in the body.

• Feeding whole grains creates more consistency in the feeding program. Since oats, barley, corn, and wheat bran are the primary grains routinely fed to horses, I've listed the basic effects of each below. It is best to try each of these grains individually or in combination to see what works best for your horse.

Oats
Oats can be fed whole or crimped. They have less energy per pound than barley or corn. Energetically, oats are warming with a sweet and slightly bitter flavor. They restore the nervous and reproductive systems, strengthen the spleen and pancreas, build and regulate Qi energy, remove cholesterol from the digestive tract and arteries, and strengthen cardiac muscles. Oats are digested in the stomach and will tend to put glucose into the circulatory system more quickly than corn or barley. For this reason they should not be fed to horses with gastric ulcers, Cushing's disease, or insulin resistance.

Barley
Barley is intermediate between oats and corn with respect to energy content. It is cooling with a sweet and salty flavor, strengthens the spleen/pancreas, regulates the stomach and fortifies the intestines, builds the blood and yin fluids and moistens dryness, promotes diuresis (urination), benefits the gall bladder and nerves, and is easily digested. I know of no contra-indications for feeding barley.

Corn
Corn is higher in both energy content and density than oats. If fed in equal volume as oats it contains twice the energy. Corn is not a heating feed, however, and it can be added to the ration during cold weather when extra energy is needed. Corn has a neutral thermal nature, sweet flavor, diuretic action, nourishes the heart, influences the stomach, improves

appetite, helps regulate digestion, promotes healthy teeth and gums, and tonifies (supports and builds up) the kidneys. There are, however, several drawbacks to corn:

- It can be contaminated with a fungus which is fatal to horses.

- Some people believe it can be high in aluminum which can interfere with proper brain function.

- It is one of the primary grains to be genetically modified, and the implication of genetically modified foods has yet to be discovered.

Wheat Bran

Wheat bran is another excellent food for horses. Due to its high phosphorus content, however, it is not a good feed for growing horses because the excess phosphorous can cause improper bone development by interfering with calcium metabolism. Bran acts as a bulk laxative when given as a mash, and, conversely, can contribute to impaction if fed dry in conjunction with inadequate water consumption.

Adding Supplements

Because of the lack of nutrition in whole grains and the lack of consistency in pelleted feeds, you will probably need to supplement the nutrients your horse receives from his regular feed. Ideally these supplements should come from whole food sources of natural vitamins and organic minerals. There are three major reasons to add feed supplements to your horse's diet:

1. ***To Replace the Nutrients Lacking in Feed:*** As discussed above, modern farming practices mean nutrient-deficient foods. To replace the missing vitamins and minerals, it is crucial to use whole food sources, not synthetic and inorganic ones. The body treats synthetic vitamins like drugs and utilizes them only if nothing else is available. In fact, the body must actually expend energy to excrete the unused portions. Horses do not absorb or assimilate minerals well unless they are in their natural chelated form. Chelated minerals, such as those found in whole food sources, are naturally bonded to other forms of nutrients, thereby enhancing their digestibility.

2. ***To Supply Extra Nutrients During Heavy Work or Recovery:*** Horses use up large quantities of nutrients during heavy exercise, especially over a long period of time. The same is also true when they are recovering from illness or injury. It is important to supply high quality nutrients in substantial quantities in each of these situations. Synthetic supplements may give a temporary boost to animals stressed from overtraining or injury so may be used as a short-term aid, if needed, in addition to whole food nutrient-dense supplements.

3. ***To Enhance Performance:*** I have found that whole food supplements provide horses with the nutrition they need to perform up to their best long-term potential. However, a short-lived boost may sometimes be noticed after giving synthetic supplements. Just remember, those effects *are* short-lived, so synthetic supplements should not be relied upon for long-term, optimum performance.

Common Supplements

Following is a list of the most common supplements on the market today, their uses and benefits.

- ***MSM:*** Supplies the antioxidant nutrient sulphur, which is needed for healthy connective tissues. It also seems to have a mild diuretic effect. It supports healthy hoof walls in some cases due to the disulphide bonds in the lamina of the hoof. I tend to use MSM for chronic muscle soreness as well.

- ***Vitamin C:*** Supports the immune system and removes free radicals.

- ***Super Oxide Dismutase:*** Scavenges free radicals.

- ***Blue-Green Algae:*** Supplies trace minerals, vitamins, and amino acids needed to help the body not only recover but maintain an optimal state of health. This particular form of algae is also very high in beta carotene, which helps neutralize the most severe free radicals in the body. Being an excellent source of chlorophyll, it also helps detoxify the horse's system.

- ***Coenzyme Q10 (CoQ10):*** This nutrient is critical to the amount of energy your horse's cells can produce. Specifically, it improves the mitochondria's ability to produce energy via the aerobic Kreb's cycle, and is therefore essential to good health on a cellular level. Without CoQ10 all energy must be produced via anaerobic metabolism, which is very ineffective and produces large amounts of lactic acid. Although CoQ10's major function in the body is to transport hydrogen for energy production, it is also a potent free radical scavenger and it can therefore be depleted when free radicals get out of control. CoQ10 is very valuable in cases of laminitis and can actually have a pain-relieving effect since it cleans up the free radicals that are rampant during laminitic inflammation. It can also be a good supplement for horses recovering from injury or who are in heavy training.

- ***Free Choice Vitamins and Minerals:*** If your horse does not have access to a natural grass pasture, I suggest offering a free choice mineral system.

- ***Probiotics:*** Probiotics are beneficial bacteria that normally live in the horse's intestines—the good guys. They help keep the gastrointestinal tract clean and healthy and produce natural antibiotics which protect the horse from pathogenic bacteria, thereby freeing the immune system to perform other important functions. They are literally the body's "first line of defense." These beneficial bacteria also produce B-Complex vitamins that are especially important during times of stress.

All probiotics need to be kept in a cool place to maintain their viability, so the tack compartment of a horse trailer is not the storage place of choice. Supplementation or replacement of beneficial bacteria is needed when the horse is stressed or drinking chlorinated water. It is also important to feed probiotics following drug or antibiotic treatment. They can be extremely helpful during allergy season (which can be year round in some locations) because of the support they give the immune system. I suggest probiotics be given on a regular basis to horses in training or recovering from illness or injury. They should be given short term to horses during any stressful event such as trailering, weaning, or deworming.

It has been my personal experience—and owners concur—that horses are more relaxed and require less feed when being offered probiotics. Many clients keep probiotic paste on hand and give it at the first signs of any digestive upset since it often gives immediate relief. I have used probiotics when treating serious colic cases, and I believe they contributed to successful outcomes. I cannot stress enough the importance of these friendly bacteria and cannot think of any situation where their use would be contra-indicated.

- ***Enzymes:*** Enzymes are an essential component of digestion. They facilitate chemical reactions that normally take place very slowly or not at all. Foods that have not been heated or processed contain enzymes that speed up their digestion after they are eaten. These same enzymes will also cause foods to spoil more rapidly, which is why processed foods, which have very few enzymes, tend to keep longer. Processing destroys all the naturally occurring enzymes in food, thus requiring the body to work harder and produce extra enzymes for digestion. If your horse is receiving only pelleted feed and dried hay, then his diet is lacking in naturally occurring food enzymes. The enzymes required to digest these foods may deplete the enzymes that would normally be used to complete other chemical reactions in the body. To avoid this, allow your horse access to whole grains and fresh grass, both of which contain enzymes. If you cannot provide these in your horse's diet, consider adding an enzyme rich supplement to the diet.

- ***Glucosamine:*** This common nutraceutical (a natural product with medicinal properties) is used in many joint support products. It has anti-inflammatory properties as well as components that provide building blocks for healthy cartilage.

- ***Essential Fatty Acids:*** Omega-3s are termed essential fatty acids (EFAs) because they are critical for good health. However, the body cannot make them on its own. For this reason, omega-3s must be obtained from food, thus making outside sources of these fats "essential." Blue-green algae, flax seed, flax seed oil, walnuts, and leafy green vegetables are all good sources of alpha-linolenic acid (ALA), the plant-based omega-3.

The Effects of Poor Nutrition

Low-level chronic health problems are becoming common due to sub-optimum nutrition. Many of these conditions are now accepted as normal, which means people have learned to settle for less than excellent health. None of these are normal; they are all signs of chronic malnutrition. A few examples that can be helped with nutritional therapy include:

- *Runny Eyes:* Watery or matted eyes often get lumped under the term "allergies," but most of the time they are the result of an imbalance in the system that can often be traced to the liver. Certain constitutional types seem predisposed to this type of imbalance or weakness, and you may find, for instance, that the problem will also be worse during certain types of weather or during certain times of the year. These types of imbalances can often be defined through Traditional Chinese Medicine, and supporting the correlating systems can then be a great help. When eye problems correlate with a liver imbalance, for instance, supporting that system becomes critical. Green foods that are rich in chlorophyll and natural antioxidants are vital. Blue-green algae, alfalfa hay in moderation, green grass (also in moderation), sprouts and carrots would all be good foods to work with in this type of imbalance. Avoiding all toxic chemicals, food additives, or drugs would also help, as these substances are very stressful to the liver.

- *Cracked and Poor-Quality Hooves:* In Traditional Chinese Medicine, the hooves as well as the tendons and ligaments are also related to the liver. As in the above example with runny eyes, it is therefore important to include green foods that support liver function. Many people suggest adding biotin to the diet for healthy hooves, but if the intestinal bacteria are healthy they will produce plenty of biotin as well as an ample supply of other B vitamins. You therefore want to make sure you support your horse's natural bacteria when you have hoof problems. Beyond that, blue-green algae is the best nutritional support for the hooves I have ever found.

- *Frequent Tendon or Ligament Injuries:* These can be related to a liver imbalance and respond to added green food in the diet. Tightness and overall muscle stiffness suggest stagnant

Liver Qi, which often resolves with supplementing natural antioxidants such as CoQ10, sprouts, and natural vitamin E.

- *Dry and/or Itchy Skin:* Fatty acids will help combat dryness. If the skin is dry but not itchy then any vegetable oil will help if added to the diet. If the skin is itchy then you must focus on oils high in omega-3 fatty acids. Flaxseed oil is good, but must be kept refrigerated. Blue-green algae is high in omega-3 fatty acids and will help many horses with itchy skin.

- *Hives:* One form of hives, or urticaria, occurs when a foreign protein enters the bloodstream. The protein acts as an antigen and the immune system forms antibodies against it. When antigen/antibody complexes are formed they must be removed from the body in the safest way possible. Since large antigen/antibody complexes can cause damage to the kidneys, it is safer for them to be moved through the lymphatic system. If the lymphatic system cannot keep up with the production of antigen/antibody complexes, they accumulate in the fluid around the cells. The extra fluid appears as welts or raised nodules. Itching may or may not be present, but generally the skin is sensitive.

  Nutritional therapy can be used in several ways to treat this condition. First, having healthy intestinal function will prevent the absorption of undigested proteins into the bloodstream (see section on leaky gut syndrome). Strong probiotics and plant-based digestive enzymes will aid the body in properly breaking down these protein molecules, thus avoiding this occurrence. If ulcers are a possibility, hold off on the enzymes and focus on healing the stomach and the intestinal lining first. Once antigen/antibody complexes are in the blood, the best way to break them down is with extra digestive enzymes. Ideally these enzymes should be given between feedings but this is not always necessary and, as noted above, they are contra-indicated in the case of ulcers.

Feeding the Fat Horse

Horses, like people, come in all shapes and sizes. Determining the ideal weight for your horse will be very helpful in keeping him healthy. Most people agree on what is too thin but people's opinion about what is too fat may vary greatly. Some people equate fat with health. Let me explain why this may not be true.

Overly fat horses are more prone to heat stress because fat acts as an insulator, holding heat in the body. Laminitis is more common in overweight horses due to the increased load on the lamina within the hoof capsule. Excess weight is hard on joints and tendons, and if your horse becomes injured and has to stay off of one leg, the other legs are more likely to break down. It can be very difficult to fit a saddle on horses with excessive fat over the withers. Also, excessively fat brood mares tend to have more difficulty with late pregnancy and delivery.

Cut back on or omit grain from the diet. Active adult horses can maintain well on roughage alone. Even then, many of our hays and grasses do not have trace minerals due to depleted soils, and stored hay is often lacking in vitamins, so many overweight horses are actually under-nourished. I would therefore suggest giving a vitamin and mineral supplement such as blue-green algae to make sure your horse gets all the nutrition he needs and to fill in any nutritional gaps in his grain or forage. You may also want to give your horse two to four tablespoons of soybean oil daily to curb his appetite. You can give this in a small bran mash or pour it directly on hay.

Ideal weight is influenced to a large extent by proper feeding and exercise, but your horse's previous management and health history may also play a role. It is my understanding that the number of fat cells an animal has determined at a young age. If you over- or under-feed young horses s will influence how they store fat when they mature. Therefore, you nt to feed your foals using the same criteria as for adults.

our horse stays fat on almost no food despite regular exercise, he may an inactive thyroid gland. Your veterinarian can run several thyroid to determine if hormone levels are constantly low. Some hypothyroid s respond to homeopathic remedies or glandular supplements to ate thyroid function. Others require daily supplementation of d hormone.

g the Thin Horse

a thin horse to gain weight can be a real challenge. A horse in optimum condition should have a thin layer of fat over the ribs and plenty of energy.

The Thin Low-Energy Horse

These horses benefit from increased calories from any source. You can increase their grain up to one-and-a-half pounds per 100 pounds of body weight. Corn and barley give more calories per pound of grain than oats. Sweet feeds will also give more energy, as will adding oil to the diet.

Probiotics and digestive enzymes will help your horse get the most from his feed. Blue-green algae will increase energy and help your horse gain weight by giving him a wide range of vitamins and minerals. Corn oil, up to one cup a day, can be added to his grain, and alfalfa hay can be given along with grass hay. If your horse is picky about eating grain he may have stomach ulcers.

The Thin High-Energy Horse

These horses fret off their weight no matter how much feed you give them. They usually respond best to lower amounts of grain. Encourage these horses to eat more hay by cutting back on the grain portion of the diet. Add fat in the form of vegetable oil or rice bran to the grain. Stay with good quality grass hay and small amounts of alfalfa. Beet pulp can also be added to the diet, but it must be soaked before it is fed. Give your horse probiotics, digestive enzymes, and blue-green algae with th cell wall removed (Cell Tech's Omega Sun algae) to provide plenty of vitamins. This form of blue-green algae will also help your horse foc and relax.

If you are feeding your horse well and have addressed all physical a mental health issues, consider acupuncture, homeopathy, or chiropra to improve his digestion and support overall health.

A Note on Grasses

When spring comes around each year and tender new buds of li bursting forth all around us, many of us are just delighted! What a time of year...except for those who have laminitis-prone horse to graze or not to graze? That is the question. What to other like a perfectly splendid pasture of fresh grass can look to the o a laminitis-prone horse like nothing more than a minefield o hazards! Before you go crazy trying to decide how to handle your horse's grazing this year, read these helpful facts about grasses. I will state the traditional beliefs about grasses and tell you whether they are true or false. You may be surprised—a lot of these facts go against decades of traditional wisdom!

TRUE *Grass founder or laminitis can happen after eating too much fresh green grass.*

Grass founder can happen for two reasons. First, the excess carbohydrates (sugars) in the grass can cause digestive upset, which often leads to laminitis. Second, grasses under stress often produce high levels of a type of sugar called fructans. Horses cannot easily digest fructans, and the sugars end up in the large intestine where bacteria multiply and break them down. The overgrowth of the fructan-digesting bacteria upsets the normal balance of the digestive tract and produces toxins that lead to laminitis.

FALSE *Grasses are high in fructans right after rain, but not during dry weather.*

Grasses produce fructans after photosynthesis, which is dependent on sunlight. Grasses are actually lower in fructans during cloudy weather.

FALSE *Grass founder or laminitis is only a problem in spring and fall, when grass is lush and growing most rapidly.*

Grasses produce fructans when stressed, which can be the result of drought, frost, or rapid growth during intense sunlight (especially after a rain).

FALSE *Laminitis-prone horses are safe in pastures that are not fertilized or maintained.*

While I prefer horses to be grazed on unfertilized, native grass pastures, grasses in nutrient-poor soil are often under stress and produce high levels of fructans. Since steadily growing grasses tend to deplete their fructan levels (which is a good thing), regular mowing to encourage this kind of growth can help control fructan levels. Regular mowing also helps control weeds.

TRUE *Overweight and insulin-resistant horses are the most susceptible to grass founder or laminitis.*
Overweight horses develop a mechanical form of laminitis from excess pressure on their laminar attachments (structures within the hoof that support the bones in the hoof). Insulin-resistant horses may or may not be overweight, but are prone to grass founder or laminitis. Signs of insulin resistance include a cresty neck and unevenly distributed fat over the withers and base of the tail.

FALSE *Hay never contains harmful carbohydrates.*
Hay can contain up to 30% fructans depending on the weather conditions when the hay was cut. Hay cut in the afternoon on a sunny day will have higher fructan levels than hay cut in the morning on a cloudy day. Hay that was rained on between cutting and baling will have the lowest fructan levels because rain washes excess fructans out of the hay. Cool climate grasses such as fescue, bromegrass, ryegrass, orchardgrass, and quackgrass tend to have higher fructan levels, while drought-resistant grasses such as bermuda, switchgrass, bluestem, and Indian grass have lower levels. All pasture grasses have the potential for high fructan levels under the right conditions.

TRUE *The safest time to turn out laminitis-prone horses on pasture is late at night or early in the mornings when the grass is not in a flowering stage of growth o[r] stressed by drought or frost.*
As stated above, these are periods when grass would contain low[er] fructan levels. Grazing muzzles are another good alternat[ive] for horses that must be left on pasture. Ideally, having a dry [lot] where you can keep your horses during critical times is bes[t.] hay causes a problem because of high fructan levels, cons[ider] soaking it for 30 minutes to an hour before feeding to was[h] some of the offending carbohydrates. Beet pulp is anothe[r] source of fiber for horses who are sensitive to carbohydra[tes.]

SECTION TWO: HUSBANDRY AND BASIC MAINTENANCE
Chapter 4
Healthy Hooves

We have all heard the expression "no hoof, no horse," but how seriously do we believe this? It is tempting to take the hoof for granted until problems develop. Since it takes a horse eight months to a year to re-grow a healthy hoof, you want to catch problems before lameness develops. Otherwise, you may have to wait a long time for your horse to become sound again. The best way to avoid problems altogether is to understand how the hoof is constructed and do everything possible to keep it healthy.

Structures In and Care of the Horse's Hoof
When we think of a horse's hoof, we tend to think of the outside of the hoof, which is called the hoof capsule, and includes the hoof wall, sole, and frog. These are all important parts of the horse's hoof. But don't forget the internal structures of the horse's hoof as well: the digital cushion, lateral cartilages, and blood vessels. We'll discuss both the outer and inner structures of the hoof below, and the best ways to take care of them.

The Hoof Capsule
The hoof capsule (hoof wall, sole, and frog) is like modified fingernail material. Both fingernails and hooves consist of flattened cells, filled with a protein called keratin. What is different about hoof is that some of the cells are arranged in tubules, while others remain stacked flat. The tubules are like little tunnels running *perpendicular* to the coronary band, and the intertubular cells are more or less *parallel* to the coronary band. This arrangement produces an internal structure similar to fiberglass.

The main function of the hoof capsule is to protect the inner soft tissues as well as to absorb concussion when the hoof strikes the ground. It also suspends the full weight of the horse by its attachments to the bony column inside. The hoof capsule must be of good quality to fulfill these functions. If it is too soft it will not protect the inner structures from bruising, and if it is too brittle it will crack and split rather than absorb shock.

Caring for the Hoof Capsule

While genetics are partially responsible for good quality hooves, excellent management and high quality nutrition are also major factors in determining the quality of foot. When the hoof capsule is strong and healthy, it will be able to withstand changes in weather and environmental conditions. Healthy hoof capsules resist moisture yet remain resilient even in hot, dry conditions. To keep your horse's hooves healthy, consider these factors:

- **High Quality Protein:** Horses need adequate, high quality protein to build a strong, healthy hoof. High quality proteins have the correct ratio of amino acids for horses and include all of the required ones, such as methionine. Feed that is high in protein does not guarantee a strong foot because it may not include all of the required components. In fact, an excessive protein diet that is not well-balanced in terms of its ingredients often leads indirectly to poorer quality feet since excess protein in general can cause more urination than is normal (extra protein is excreted in urine). If a horse is kept in a stall, this excess urination causes the stall to become wet, and the ammonia in urine is caustic to hooves. Most adult horses do not need more than 10% protein in their diet. Whole grains and blue-green algae are excellent natural sources of protein that provide amino acids in the correct ratio for horses.

- **Trace Minerals:** Trace minerals, such as sulphur, are important for hoof quality, and, like protein, must be fed in a form that is digestible and appropriate for horses. Since most free-choice mineral blocks or powders are designed for cattle, research your mineral supplements carefully before buying. In addition, because some minerals are more expensive than others, certain formulated supplements are composed mostly of the cheaper minerals and contain very little of the more expensive ones. These financially dictated formulas can wreak havoc on your horse's mineral balance and will sometimes create deficiencies even if you feed your horse the recommended quantity. While there are numerous supplements on the market that claim to improve hoof quality, the only ones that have produced consistent results in my practice are Farrier's Formula and blue-green algae. In extreme cases, I have combined these two supplements with excellent results.

- **Probiotics:** If your horse is on a solid whole grain diet with high quality supplements and still has bad feet, you may want to add a probiotic such as Fastrack. Probiotics help establish colonies of beneficial bacteria in your horse's intestinal tract that in turn produce the vitamin biotin, which is crucial for healthy hooves. If your horse becomes stressed or for any reason does not have sufficient beneficial bacteria in his intestines, he will be deficient in biotin, which leads to poor quality hooves. Probiotics also help your horse assimilate nutrients from his feed and supplements. I've found that it's much more effective to feed probiotics along with a good diet and whole food supplement (like blue-green algae) than it is to try and guess which particular nutrients are missing from the diet.

- **Management:** The best way to manage your horse's hooves is to keep their moisture content consistent with the ground on which you expect your horse to live and work. For instance, if you live in a dry climate with hard, rocky ground, then keep your horse's hooves dry and hard. Overall, hooves are easiest to maintain under dry conditions since it's easier to add moisture than to take it away.

Repeated wet and dry cycles are the hardest on the hoof. For instance, if your horse has been living in wet conditions and then your area experiences a drought, the ground will dry out and become much harder. Your horse's feet will take longer than the ground to dry out, and during the transition they will be susceptible to bruising. During the transition you might want to paint the soles with a drying/antiseptic agent. There are many on the market including Kopertox and Durasole. A 7% iodine solution also works, but must be used with extreme caution to protect both the skin and hair of human and animal alike, and also the eyes (from splatter). An effective way of applying these liquids is using a dabber or a small syringe, dribbling on light coats that dry quickly. These chemicals should be used in the short term only as they can be toxic to the horse and humans.

In general, keep your horse's hooves as dry and clean as possible. If your horse is stalled, keep the bedding clean and dry since soft, wet feet are prone to infection from bacteria and fungus in contaminated bedding.

If you live in an extremely arid or desert-like climate, you may want to moisten your horse's hooves slightly either by overflowing the water trough periodically so your horse has to stand in a muddy patch to drink, or by applying a moisturizing hoof dressing. Non-greasy formulas such as Rain Maker are best for adding moisture to a dry hoof. Greasy dressings can help retain moisture, but aren't as good for hydrating an already dry hoof because they do not contain water. You might consider moistening your horse's feet a day or two before the farrier comes to trim—it will make his or her job a lot easier! It will only take a few days for those hooves to return to their normal desert dry.

The basic rule of thumb when it comes to care of the hoof capsule is consistent observation and treatment. When your area experiences changes in moisture, keep an eye on the amount of moisture in your horse's hooves, and use the recommendations above to make the transition smoother and easier.

- **Homeopathy:** If your horse still has poor quality hooves, even with an excellent diet, high quality supplements, and careful management, you may want to consider a homeopathic consultation. This kind of consultation and treatment can help locate the source of the problem (which might include poor digestion or reaction to vaccination), and treat it gently and non-invasively.

The Internal Structures of the Hoof

The most important internal structures in the hoof are the:

- **Digital Cushion:** A pad of live tissue just underneath the frog that provides the primary support for the frog.

- **Lateral Cartilages:** Structural support for the entire hoof, growing from the digital cushion to just above the coronary band (you can feel the lateral cartilages by feeling for hard structures just under the skin above the coronary band).

- **Blood Vessels:** A network running through the digital cushion and lateral cartilage supplying nutrients to the entire foot and also helping absorb shock when the foot hits the ground.

Caring for the Internal Structures of the Hoof

In addition to the nutritional tips given above, which will contribute to the health of the internal structures of the hoof, exercise and environment are the two most important factors to consider in formulating a good hoof care program.

How do exercise and environment affect these internal hoof structures? Through *stimulation*. According to research by Dr. Robert M. Bowker, V.M.D., Ph.D., the greater the stimulation to the frog and sole, the more these internal structures grow in strength and mass. High levels of stimulation produce well-developed lateral cartilages, a strong digital cushion, and, most importantly, highly developed blood vessels with many branches. Microscopic studies show that well-stimulated hooves develop an entire web of blood vessels while poorly stimulated hooves have only a few large vessels with very little branching. All this branching means more blood in the hoof, with the blood providing a liquid "cushion" that absorbs the impact of the hoof hitting the ground. Without proper cushioning from all three of these hoof structures, the pressure from impact gets spread to other parts of the hoof and leg that are not meant to absorb that kind of shock. This can result in lameness and deterioration of your horse's joints and hooves.

To get proper stimulation, the frog and sole have to actually make contact with the ground, which doesn't happen with most types of shoeing. In a wild setting, horses get constant stimulation on the frogs and soles of their feet because they don't wear shoes, and because they travel up to 25 miles a day. But most domesticated horses

Cross section of hoof.

are shod, confined to stalls most of the day, and ridden in soft arenas that provide little or no stimulation. Shoes elevate the foot off the ground, so the frog and sole can't make contact or get stimulation. Plus, the soft footing and lack of movement further limit stimulation. The result is a weakened hoof.

What can you do to give your horse's feet proper stimulation? You can remove your horse's shoes and let him go barefoot, or you can use special pads to increase frog stimulation for shod horses. The third option, especially for horses who have innately good feet, is to keep them shod without special pads and ride them on rough and varied terrain. (Note: There are many schools of barefoot trimming; if you decide to "go barefoot" be sure you research methodology and choose a farrier whose work comes well recommended.)

You'll also want to make sure that your horse is shod or trimmed so that he makes contact with his heel first, and that both his frog and bars actually make contact with the ground (or a pad). In addition, his frog should be large and firm with a shallow center sulcus (the crack in the middle of the frog), and the bars should be angled rather than being upright or vertical. This type of foot is best designed to dissipate force and support the weight of the horse.

Once you've corrected your horse's shoeing situation so he can get proper frog stimulation, you need to make sure he gets plenty of exercise, which increases the amount of actual frog stimulation. The more times your horse has to pick up and put down his feet, the more stimulation he's getting on his frogs. Finally, adding plenty of turnout time to his daily regimen will also help.

Common Hoof Ailments

While we all try our best to manage our horse's feet properly and feed the highest quality grains and supplements, chances are we may still encounter one or more common hoof ailments. Here's a short list with practical instructions on how to deal with the most common and acute ailments.

Stone Bruises

If your horse lacks adequate sole thickness, he will be prone to bruising. Flat footed horses are also more prone to bruising. Use hoof testers to localize the area of soreness and very gently pare with a hoof knife to uncover the extent of the bruised area. If the bruising is in a half-moon shape across the entire toe, it indicates a more serious internal problem with the hoof (consult your farrier or veterinarian if this is the case). Otherwise, the best treatment for bruising is protection in the form of a boot or pad.

The homeopathic remedy Arnica is very helpful in simple bruising. This remedy helps the body reabsorb the blood or serum from a bruised area, which helps speed healing and reduces pain. If a bruise is particularly painful, you can soak the foot in a saturated solution of Epsom salts to decrease the soreness. If your horse won't hold his foot in a bucket, you can put two to three tablespoons of dry Epsom salts in a few ounces of water and wrap this onto his foot or put it in the bottom of a boot.

Sometimes horses can get very deep bruises, especially if they lose a shoe on rough ground. These deep bruises also occur after extended periods of wet weather followed by hot, dry weather. During the wet weather, the horse's feet soften then get badly bruised as the ground gets hard and uneven. Sometimes these bruises don't show up with a hoof tester because they are so deep. Suspect a deep bruise if your horse is lame on one foot and has an increased digital pulse but no obvious heat or swelling. Regular soaking in Epsom salts and two to three weeks off will generally resolve a deep bruise.

Abscesses

A hoof abscess will generally be hotter and more painful than a bruise, and you may find swelling above the hoof. Again, use hoof testers to locate the abscess and a hoof knife to open the abscess so it can drain. Once an abscess has been opened and drained, keep the hoof bandaged until healing is complete. Epsom salt soaks or poultices can be used if your horse is still sore after the abscess is opened. A tetanus toxoid shot should be given if your horse has not had one in the previous year. I do not recommend antibiotics since they actually interfere with the natural maturing process of the abscess, and since most abscesses will resolve quickly once they open and drain. Homeopathy can also be used for stubborn cases.

Cracks

In my experience, these are almost always due to injury or unbalanced feet. A healthy hoof should not crack. If your horse has an otherwise healthy hoof, examine the coronary band carefully above the crack. It will generally be jammed up higher than the adjacent area. Corrective shoeing may be needed to alleviate this condition.

Thrush

This is a bacterial or fungal infection of the foot that can be extremely painful. The affected horse will have a foul smelling dark discharge around the frog. The tissue around the frog and heel will also appear very unhealthy. These horses should be moved to a dry area and the foot should be cleaned daily. Water and a mild soap is your best choice for cleaning the greasy discharge. Use a soft scrub brush to get into the crevices. You may need your farrier to trim the frog back to healthy tissue, as any dead tissue contributes to bacterial growth and makes it harder to clean the area. Because thrush can be related to a weakened immune system, it is a good idea to evaluate your horse's rations and consider a supplement such as blue-green algae.

Thrush Case Study

To help you further understand how to deal with thrush, I've included a case study on the subject written by farrier Cecilia Adamson. This case deals with chronic, persistent thrush deep in the central sulcus of the frog. This is actually a fairly common problem that often goes unrecognized by both farriers and horse owners alike. The horse in this case is a Tennessee Walker mare who was barefoot and not being worked. She had fairly narrow, oblong feet with narrow frogs and compressed heels. She was sound at the time, but she might have gone lame had she been required to work.

Here's what Cecilia has to say…

As I was trimming this horse's feet, I noticed that she had a very deep split in the center of the frog. Chronic thrush had developed in the split, and the depth of the split made it very, very hard to treat. In fact, the split was so deep that it reached all the way into the live tissues of the hoof. To treat this case, I used persistent daily treatments to quell the thrush and return the hoof back to soundness. The treatment I used consisted of the following, daily:

1. *I flushed the area with hydrogen peroxide to clean and boil out dirt and debris, and then dried the area inside thoroughly with clean cotton cloths or Q-tips until they came out clean. The goal here was to get the area as clean and dry as possible.*

2. *Next, I put Betadine ointment on a length of cotton or gauze and pushed it up into the split in the frog. I also soaked the area with Betadine solution. The gauze acted as a barrier to keep dirt and manure out of the split and*

also held the split open to the air. Otherwise, the split might have closed over and the infection could have gotten worse. I wanted the split to heal from the inside out, not the outside in.

As her hooves began to heal, it became more and more difficult to push the gauze into the split. This told me that the frog was beginning to heal from the inside out. The key to success in this case was using the treatment every single day. Missing even one day would have permitted the thrush to worsen.

At the time I treated this horse, I didn't have the benefit of all the knowledge I have now. When I treat this kind of condition today, I use many other healing approaches in addition to peroxide and Betadine.

I prefer it if horses can go barefoot during the healing process (ideally, six to eight weeks). Barefoot horses get much more stimulation of the frog and heel, which increases circulation and promotes faster healing. I would also suggest frequent trimming to keep the split open and the frog and heel function optimal. Ideally, a healthy frog should be two-thirds as wide at the base as it is long. Most of the time, horses with this condition have narrow frogs and compressed heels because they have been shod and lack frog/heel stimulation.

 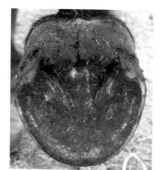

Hoof with narrow frog.   **Hoof with healthy frog.**

If it is not possible to keep the horse barefoot, then I would suggest shoeing the horse with a Natural Balance pad and dental impression material. This combination simulates contact with the ground, so that the heels and frogs get a lot of stimulation even though they are not in actual contact with the ground. Keep in mind that you need to work with an educated farrier when using this approach—these tools, like any other, can be either helpful or destructive depending on who is using them.

Finally, supplemental nutrition and exercise are keys to healing. Healing requires a lot of nutrients, and there is no better source for whole food nutrition than blue-green algae. Probiotics are also essential to encourage healthy hoof growth. In addition, regular exercise increases the stimulation of frog and heels, promoting rapid healing and hoof growth.

If you're not sure if your horse has this condition (and many farriers even miss it), look for narrow frogs and heels, curved bars and a deep split in the frog (you'll be able to push your hoof pick quite deep into the center line of the frog). You might also want to look for separate up-and-down movement in the bulbs of the heels, with one bulb moving up while the other moves down. This would indicate a breakdown in the connective tissues.

In Review: When working with this most-difficult-of-areas to heal, one must be tenacious. Treatment must continue daily for as long as it takes. Another option for medication includes apple cider vinegar mixed in a ratio of ten parts to one part tea tree oil. This mixture is best applied with a spray bottle. After the hoof dries, you can follow with a mixture of ten parts olive oil, one part tea tree oil, and a bit of cayenne pepper to stimulate the circulation.

Doing *all* of the cleaning, drying, and medicating steps is imperative to the successful annihilation of this disease. Thrush can be overcome, but it takes work and dedication. Ignore anyone who says it is chronic and can't be cleared up because it can be!

Chapter 5
Joint Health

Joint Health for Young Horses

The 2005 Surpass Equine Arthritis Survey[1] indicates that one of two horse owners in the United States has a horse affected with lameness, and that two-thirds of those owners point to joint rather than hoof pain as the cause of the problem. Obviously joint health has become such a major area of concern for performance horse owners that it deserves some serious attention. While many horse owners now consider it normal and acceptable to give joint injections to four- and five-year-old horses, my clinical experience shows me that horses should not need this kind of support until much later in life, if ever. With excellent management and nutritional support, it is possible for even hard working performance horses to have strong healthy joints for many years.

What Causes Joint Problems?

To understand how to create and maintain good joint health, you have to understand the causes of joint problems. Basically, if the joint fluid stays thick, it can properly lubricate the joint and keep the cartilage healthy. It is when the joint fluid becomes thin that joint problems develop. What causes joint fluid to become thin? Lack of antioxidants!

Horses start developing joint problems (whether they are noticeable yet or not) when they begin training or exercising hard. When horses exercise hard, their bodies create more free radicals than usual, which then use up their supply of natural antioxidants at a faster rate. When the body has more free radicals than it has antioxidants, one area that suffers is the joint fluid, which changes in consistency and becomes thin. When this happens the joint fluid cannot properly lubricate the joint, causing wear and tear on the cartilage. As the cartilage wears down, the joint becomes less and less stable. To compensate, the body lays bone down around the joint to try to stabilize it. At this point, the joint develops calcium deposits and you can see structural changes on X-rays.

Creating Joint Health from the Beginning

One of the best ways to create a foundation for joint health is to start

[1]Sponsored by Idexx Laboratories (http://www.compendiumvet.com/PV_605news10.html)

before the foal is even born. Make sure that the pregnant mare has plenty of vitamins, minerals, and trace minerals throughout the pregnancy so that the foal develops good bones and joints. Once the foal is born it is difficult to supplement trace minerals while he is nursing, and mare's milk contains mainly macro minerals like calcium. Then, as soon as the foal starts to eat some grain be sure and start him on good micro-mineral supplements, especially if good quality grass is not available.

One of the best and easiest ways to ensure that mare and foal get all the micronutrients they need is to feed blue-green algae because it is balanced in calcium and phosphorous. You can also feed the pregnant mare some alfalfa for its micronutrient and calcium content, but don't feed alfalfa to young foals since its calcium and phosphorous ratio is not balanced.

Joint Health in Growing Horses
To keep joints healthy in young horses, feed plenty of micronutrients (from blue-green algae, for instance), and avoid overloading the diet with too many calories. Studies have linked diets high in carbohydrates with developmental bone problems like Osteo Chondrosis Dissecans (OCD). Plus, overfed young horses who are too fat will overstress their joints with the extra weight. As a general rule, on young horses I like to be able to feel ribs but not see them. You will also want to monitor the young horse's exercise regimen carefully. Young horses are not fully developed until they are four years of age so, while you can certainly start working them earlier, they are not strong enough to handle heavy work until age four.

Joint Health in Horses Ages Four to Six
At this age, horses are able to handle a full training schedule and start exercising heavily. To support this transition, supplement the feed with good quality trace minerals, preferably from whole food sources. Since your horse is exercising hard, you will also want to add antioxidants to his diet in order to neutralize the free radicals being produced from the heavy exercise. Good antioxidants include blue-green algae (which has beta carotene), noni juice, super oxide dismutase, coenzyme Q10, grape seed extract, omega-3 fatty acids, and certain minerals such as sulphur (found in the supplement MSM). Stick with natural antioxidant supplements (i.e., those in their natural form) as much as possible since

the body can use naturally occurring antioxidants more efficiently than synthetic ones.

At this point in your horse's life you want to focus on good nutrition and antioxidants to prevent cartilage damage. Joint supplements like glucosamine (which is a single component of the cartilage) are not particularly helpful by themselves. They will not prevent cartilage damage—antioxidants do a much better job of that. In fact, it is best to delay the use of joint supplements as long as possible using the methods discussed above. Please note that it is not normal for horses to develop joint problems at this age. Joint problems at this age indicate a lack of nutrition, specifically antioxidants.

Hyaluronic acid can also be injected into the joints, and is one substance that can be used to prevent cartilage wear and tear and reduce inflammation after a joint has already been damaged. Hyaluronic acid will thicken the joint fluid and decrease inflammation in the joint (which is the result of free radicals that can thin the joint fluid). If your horse is a little sore after a particularly hard workout or show, you may want to consider giving him Legend, which is an intravenous hyaluronic injection, instead of going immediately to a joint injection. Remember that you can only give your horse so many joint injections in his lifetime, and that each injection increases the chances of introducing infection. Overall, if you have the choice, use excellent nutrition and antioxidants before resorting to joint injections.

Just to give you an example of how a young horse might be worked and supplemented, consider my mule Jake. When Jake was four years old I worked him five times a week for an hour per session. He was learning to get his hind end up underneath him, how to back up, and generally how to use his body correctly. He was building up his strength and learning to carry himself, which can be hard work. I fed him probiotics, blue-green algae, and noni juice twice a day. If he had a hard workout, he received regular Bowen sessions (see Bodywork). Although every horse is different, this example should give you a good idea of where to start when designing a program for your young horse's optimal joint health.

Joint Health for Horses Ages Six and Up
While the right nutrition is important for creating healthy joints in young horses, it becomes absolutely essential for maintaining healthy joints as

horses move into performance work. Nutrition is a proactive way to keep joints from deteriorating even during heavy work. In addition, as horses progress in their athletic careers you may need to use a different set of nutrients to address thinning of the joint fluid or damage to the cartilage while still providing solid nutrition and plenty of antioxidants to prevent any further damage.

Depending on whether your horse is experiencing any changes in his joints, you may need to offer cartilage support in the form of a joint supplement. Here are some factors you might want to keep in mind when deciding what kinds of joint supplements and nutrition to feed your horse.

Supplements for Healthy Joint Fluid
Keeping the joint fluid thick is the first step to maintaining healthy joints. Working horses need access to plenty of naturally occurring antioxidants to neutralize the free radicals being produced from heavy exercise. Consider using blue-green algae, noni juice, super oxide dismutase, vitamin C, vitamin E, coenzyme Q10, grape seed extract, omega-3 fatty acids, and certain minerals such as sulphur (found in the supplement MSM).

Supplements for Healthy Joint Cartilage
There are three primary components in joint cartilage— glucosamine hydrochloride, chondroitin sulphate, and polysulfated glycosaminoglycans (PSGAG). Most joint supplements combine glucosamine with chondroitin sulphate, and the best ones also include micronutrients and antioxidants (which helps your horse make the best use of the glucosamine and chondroitin sulphate). Remember that nutrition involves complex relationships, and no single nutrient functions alone in the body. If you've already been feeding your horse a diet high in micronutrients and antioxidants, just add glucosamine. Adequan, an injectable solution, contains only the third element of joint cartilage (PSGAGs), and may be a good option if you don't think your horse will eat oral supplements or absorb them. Keep in mind, though, that no amount of joint supplements will keep your horse's joints healthy if you're not feeding him a high quality diet filled with micronutrients and antioxidants.

Anti-Inflammatory Supplements

If your horse does have arthritis or damage in the joints, you may need to support him with non-steroidal anti-inflammatory agents like Bute or Banamine, which help with the pain. Keep in mind, however, that horses can experience long-term side effects from prolonged use of these kinds of products. These products do not stop the degradation of the joint or aid in healing. To assist with the healing process, try yucca or devil's claw, both of which are anti-inflammatory herbs that can actually slow the deterioration of the joint. Remember that once a joint becomes damaged it takes a long time to heal. That's why it is so important to provide your horse with the maximum quality and quantity of nutrients needed to maintain joint health throughout his life.

Quick Reference Guide to Supplements for Joint Health

- ***Adequan:*** This is an injectable solution containing PSGAGs (a component of joint cartilage) that may be a good option if you don't think your horse will eat oral supplements or may not absorb them.

- ***Antioxidants:*** These neutralize the free radicals that are produced from heavy exercise, which can thin the joint fluid. Naturally occurring antioxidants include blue-green algae, noni juice, super oxide dismutase, vitamin C, vitamin E, coenzyme Q10, grape seed extract, omega-3 fatty acids, and certain minerals such as sulphur.

- ***Bute and Banamine:*** These are both non-steroidal anti-inflammatory drugs with effects similar to aspirin. They offer pain relief but can have many side effects and interfere with healing.

- ***Chondroitin Sulphate:*** This is a single component of joint cartilage. The body cannot effectively use this component by itself, so look for a supplement that combines glucosamine with chondroitin sulphate, minerals, and antioxidants.

- ***Devil's Claw:*** This herb supports the digestive, urinary, and circulatory systems and has an anti-inflammatory, analgesic, sedative, and diuretic action. Devil's claw can be fed in combination with yucca in B-L solution or Bounce Back, or individually. Devil's claw is not as irritating to the horse as the non-steroidal anti-inflammatories, but if the horse has ulcers it can aggravate them, which might be an indication to give yucca by itself.

- **Glucosamine:** This is a single component of joint cartilage. The body cannot effectively use this component by itself, so look for a supplement that combines glucosamine with chondroitin sulphate, minerals, and antioxidants.

- **Hyaluronic Acid:** This is a substance that can be injected directly into the joint, often combined with steroids if there is inflammation. Remember, if you have the choice, use excellent nutrition and antioxidants before resorting to joint injections.

- **Legend:** An intravenous injection composed of hyaluronic acid, which will thicken the joint fluid and decrease inflammation in the joint. Legend can be used if your horse is sore after a particularly hard workout or show.

- **MSM:** This supplement contains high levels of the antioxidant mineral sulphur, which is generally more supportive of muscles and connective tissues than joints. However, sulphur is a component of cartilage and also an antioxidant so it can be helpful in preventing joint damage.

- **Yucca:** Yucca is an herb that contains organic steroidal saponins. A saponin effect allows a cleansing penetration and dispersal of digestive enzymes, and the steroidal effect limits inflammation. The feeding of yucca can be against some medication rules in performance situations, so if you are competing be sure and check this out. Yucca can be fed in combination with Devil's Claw in B-L solution, or individually.

Bodywork

Amidst all this discussion about nutritional supplements for joint health, don't forget bodywork for your horse! Bodywork keeps the connective tissues in your horse's body supple, and chiropractic work, specifically, keeps the spine straight. If your horse has tightness or stiffness in the body from sore muscles or a subluxation in the spine, it can put uneven stress on his limbs, causing uneven pressure on the joints. This uneven pressure will eventually cause damage to the joint fluid and cartilage. In these cases, joint supplements and the best nutrition cannot prevent joint damage because you haven't addressed the cause. That's why bodywork is so important. In addition to chiropractic and osteopathy, which should be done by a medical professional, there are many other supportive therapies that you can learn yourself or have done by someone with training. The following are some of the modalities that my clients and I have found helpful:

Massage

Massage has been used for therapeutic purposes for hundreds of years and there are many documented benefits of this treatment modality. Fortunately, there are many massage techniques that have been adapted to horses. Among the many documented benefits of massage are:

- Enhancing muscle tone and range of motion

- Reducing inflammation and swelling in the joints, thereby alleviating pain

- Promoting the healing process by increasing the flow of nutrients in the muscles and aiding and carrying away excessive fluids and toxins

Equine Acupressure

Based on Traditional Chinese Medicine and the energy meridians of the body, this modality is a noninvasive, deceptively gentle process that can profoundly impact humans and animals. By applying gentle pressure with the hands or fingers on specific points on the horse's body, one can effectively participate in his health and well being, contributing to years of quality performance and pleasure riding. As reported in *Equine Acupressure – A Working Manual*, by Nancy Zidonis, Amy Snow, and Marie Soderberg, its effects have consistently shown its ability to:

- Release endorphins necessary to reduce pain

- Relieve muscle spasms

- Resolve injuries more readily by removing toxins and increasing blood supply

- Enhance mental clarity required for focus in training and performance

- Release natural cortisone to reduce swelling

- Build the body's immune system

If you want a technique that you can use yourself in enhancing your horse's well-being, acupressure may become an invaluable tool for you.

Equine Touch

Equine Touch is a non-diagnostic, noninvasive, energy and connective soft tissue discipline which works at a complete holistic level; that is, it addresses the equine as a whole without paying any particular attention to any named problem as such. The technique consists of a series of gentle, vibrational moves performed over specific points in specific choreographed patterns and has the effect of releasing spasms, distortions, and adhesions in the connective tissue and smooth muscle of organs. This synergistic approach influences the body and systems to return to balance in a natural way. The method was devised by Jock Ruddock and was based on his prior education in the Bowen method and other bodywork techniques.

TTEAM: The Tellington-Jones Equine Awareness Method

Originally devised for horses, this method, originated by Linda Tellington-Jones, is now also applied to animals of just about every species and is practiced worldwide. For the horses, it involves bodywork (TTouch), groundwork, and under-saddle work and has been phenomenally successful in improving performance and attitude. Although it is a comprehensive approach, it includes many exercises for addressing specific common problems such as loading, sitting back, difficulties with clipping or worming, biting, kicking, and more. It can also be a wonderful resource when you're troubleshooting a difficult issue with your horse. TTEAM is a great tool to help you work more effectively with your horse and form a closer partnership, and books, tapes, and classes are readily available and easy to find.

Touch Balancing/Animal Bowen

This is an adaptation of the Bowen/Bowtech Technique for humans to the physiology and anatomy of animals. As developed and taught by Carol Bennett, the purpose of this technique is to relax inappropriate muscle tension, which can be the cause of an animal's poor performance or the beginning of a more serious health challenge, and to facilitate balance of the body. As stated in *Bowen Hands*, the official publication of the Bowen Academy of Australia, By Dr. Portia Reading:

- Animals treated with the Bowen Technique show a general improvement in well-being and can show relief from signs such as lameness, malaise, digestive problems, allergies, skin conditions, etc.

- The gentle moves on soft tissue appear to restore balance to musculoskeletal, autonomic and meridian systems equally for humans and animals.

- Bowtech for animals appears to also produce an integrated response, improving circulation, lymphatic and venous drainage, and helping in the assimilation of nutrients and elimination of toxins.

Chapter 6
Vaccinations

I was taught in veterinary school that vaccinations could do no harm and were very effective in preventing disease. For the first ten years of my practice, I encouraged owners to vaccinate for encephalomyelitis, tetanus, and rabies once a year, and influenza and rhinopneumonitis twice a year. Pregnant mares were vaccinated for rhinopneumonitis at five, seven, and nine months of pregnancy. I never saw a case of encephalomyelitis, tetanus, or rabies, and I believe the incidence of full-blown cases of flu and rhinopneumonitis were decreased in vaccinated horses.

At the same time, though, I was kept very busy treating colic, laminitis, sick foals, and chronic respiratory infections. Around 1990 I read my first article suggesting that vaccinations could have some negative effects on a horse's health. My initial reaction was one of disbelief and anger at the idea. Once this seed was planted, however, I could no longer deny that vaccinations often did aggravate symptoms in some chronically ill horses.

At the time, my partner and I had 20 horses. One year, after some serious soul searching, we elected to skip their annual boosters. To our amazement not only did the horses stay healthy, but their health actually improved. Several of these horses had a tendency to colic, and they began colicking less frequently or not at all. Two horses had chronic laminitis, and both of these improved steadily—one was even able to go back into training. Several of the horses did contract a respiratory infection at a local show, but vaccinated horses at other barns in the area were also affected. Hair coat, hooves, and feed efficiency also improved. About one year after our decision to skip vaccinations, we had an encephalomyelitis scare so we boostered all the horses with Eastern and Western encephalomyelitis and tetanus. Within 30 days, both foundered horses relapsed, and the number of colicked horses was back up.

This experience made a believer out of me, and from that point on I advised my clients to tailor their vaccination programs to the individual needs of their horses and to cease vaccinating any horse with a chronic illness. After four years of fewer vaccinations and lower drug use, I noticed that I was treating fewer laminitis cases, fewer and milder colics, and had healthier patients overall. There is no doubt that vaccinations can overwhelm the immune system, especially if it is already weakened by chronic disease. In healthy individuals excessive vaccination can actually create a disease state called vaccinosis. Symptoms of vaccinosis can vary greatly but include dry hair coat, weak hooves, skin eruptions, sarcoids (skin tumors), and warts.

There is much we need to learn about the effectiveness and safety of vaccines. Drug companies do not test vaccines to see how long they are effective, so **checking "titers"** on horses may be a way to avoid annual vaccinations. Vaccination programs should be geared to fit each individual situation. In addition, as covered in the "Introduction to Holistic Healing" and "Nutrition" sections of this book, boosting the body's immune response holistically is the best way to ensure your horse's resistance to diseases.

A Quick Note on Titers

Titers are blood tests that measure antibody levels in the blood, and are most commonly used for determining immunity to rabies, encephalitis, and tetanus. If you truly want to avoid vaccines, you can have titers done to show whether or not your horse has developed an antibody response against certain diseases from previous vaccinations (some vaccines create a lifelong immunity).

A negative titer doesn't necessarily mean your horse is not protected, nor does a positive one show that he absolutely is protected. But a positive titer does suggest that additional vaccines are not needed at that time. Titers are less reliable for influenza and rhinopneumonitis. A titer is an extra step you can take to help convince a barn owner in a boarding situation that you are not just trying to save money by choosing not to vaccinate, since a titer costs more than the vaccine.

Vaccination and Chronic Disease

In my experience, chronic disease occurs more frequently in heavily vaccinated horses, and I believe I know why this happens. To understand why this occurs though, you must first understand how vaccinations work. The actual vaccine injected into the horse does not in and of itself provide protection from disease. This is very important to understand. It is the response of the individual horse's immune system to the vaccine that determines whether or not the horse will be protected.

The vaccine is an antigen designed to trigger a specific antibody reaction so that the next time the immune system "sees" this antigen it will react quickly to combat it. This sounds like a great plan and, with a good quality vaccine and a strong immune system, has the potential to work. The problem is that many diseases don't produce good antigens, so toxic substances called adjuvants must be added to the vaccine in order to trigger a reaction by the immune system. These adjuvants can take several forms, including toxic heavy metals like mercury, and can cause their own problems, sometimes quite serious. Also, the immunity following many vaccines is very short-lived, requiring injections to be given as often as every two months. Would you allow yourself to be vaccinated every two months?

Here is a metaphor of the havoc multiple vaccines can cause. Consider the body as a country and the immune system as the army and local police in charge of protecting it. The nervous system acts as the communication network and the circulatory system makes up the highways. The army regularly protects the borders, and the police keep internal peace. Everything goes well until, without warning, there is a huge invasion of enemy paratroopers (say you inject your horse with VEW-T, Flu, Rhino, Rabies, Strangles, and Potomac Horse Fever vaccines on the same day). These invaders use the established, heretofore safe, highway system to infiltrate all areas of the country and come in several shapes and sizes, requiring specialty forces to combat them. Now, if we have a very strong army and police force, with lots of highly trained specialists, the invasion will be thwarted. However, border patrol and local peace keeping efforts may suffer temporarily. This is why it is important to give your horse several days off after any vaccine and to try not to give too many vaccinations at the same time.

If your horse has a marginal or weak immune system, a whole different scenario may occur. Because there are no reserve soldiers, all forces are withdrawn from their regular duties to fight the invasion. Communications may break down as chaos develops (such as chronic herpes). In the confusion, orders may be given to attack friendly forces (auto-immune disease such as periodic ophthalmia). Stressed soldiers may become trigger happy and shoot at anything they see (allergy symptoms). Even if the war is won, it is often at great expense, as criminals have taken over many cities while the police force was preoccupied (a good example is cancer). Remember, even though this is just a vaccine, it is designed to trick the immune system into thinking it is the real disease. With na infection there would rarely be more than one real disease at a time.

To give you an overall perspective on how the horse's immune system works when dealing with the "invaders," I've included a typical vaccination history below. Vaccines were started on this horse when she was young and in good health. Check out the final result at the end of the list:

- August 1989: Flu, Rhino
- November 1989: VEW-T, Flu, Rhino, Rabies, Strangles
- December 1989: Flu, Rhino
- April 1989: Flu, Rhino
- August 1990: Flu, Rhino
- December 1990: VEW-T
- January 1991: Flu, Rhino
- October 1991: Flu, Rhino
- February 1992: VEW-T, Rabies, Strangles, Potomac Horse Fever
- July 1992: Flu, Rhino
- December 1992: Flu, Rhino, Strangles
- May 1993: VEW-T, Rabies, Potomac Horse Fever
- June 1993: Flu, Rhino, Strangles
- ***August 1993: Removed Melanomas Surgically***
- September 1993: Flu, Rhino
- March 1994: Flu, Rhino
- May 1994: VEW-T, Rabies, Potomac Horse Fever
- ***July 1994: Laminitis***
- ***September 1994: Laminitis***
- ***December 1994: Flu, Rhino—Horse Still Under Treatment for Laminitis***
- March 1995: Flu, Rhino
- May 1996: VEW-T, Flu, Rhino, Rabies, Strangles, Potomac Horse Fever
- ***August 1996: Colic***
- January 1997: VEW-T, Flu, Rhino, Rabies, Strangles, Potomac Horse Fever
- ***July 1997: Return of Melanomas and Severe Laminitis***
- ***September 1997: Laminitis***—Since the horse did not respond to conventional treatment, a holistic approach was

‌ all vaccines discontinued. She responded well and
‌ further signs of chronic disease.

‌*y 2006: Horse is Still Doing Well, No Vaccines, ‌vo Chronic Diseases*

At a 2004 American Holistic Veterinary Medical Association conference in Kansas City, Missouri, Dr. W. Jean Dodds, a well known research veterinarian, spoke about her extensive work on the potential long-term adverse reactions to vaccination. Dr. Dodds has extensive case studies to support the connection between auto-immune thyroiditis and behavior changes in dogs. Her research indicates problems from vaccines may not manifest at the time of vaccination but may increase the animal's susceptibility to chronic disease later in life. Her accumulated evidence indicates that vaccination protocols should no longer be considered a one-size-fits-all program.

Which Vaccinations Should You Give Your Horse?

I can't say this strongly enough: It is critical that the status of your horse's immune system and the risk of his exposure to diseases be carefully evaluated before any vaccines are given! To decide how to tailor your vaccination program to your horse's needs, ask yourself the questions below:

1. How old is your horse?

2. How healthy is your horse?

3. What diseases are present in your area?

4. Where and how is your horse stabled?

5. What activities do you and your horse participate in?

6. How fearful are you that your horse will get sick or die if you do not vaccinate?

7. Are you willing to change your management, if necessary, to prevent disease and support your horse's immune system?

Once you answer these questions, you can work with your veterinarian to create a vaccination program that works for you and your horse. (Hopefully your veterinarian will be educated in or open to your holistic approach.) In addition to his professional input, it is also important for you to educate yourself about the common equine diseases so you can take an active and empowered role in the final decision. Here's a quick-start guide to the more common equine diseases and their vaccines to help you get started.

Encephalitis

I recommend vaccinating healthy horses for this disease as it can be fatal. Equine encephalitis comes in three forms: Eastern, Western, and Venezuelan. Therefore, all three are combined, along with tetanus toxoid, in one vaccine. This is commonly referred to as a VEW-T vaccine. Equine encephalitis is a viral disease transmitted to the horse by mosquitoes, which pick up the virus from intermediate hosts such as birds, small rodents, and reptiles. This means your horse does not get this infection from or give it to other horses, so even a backyard horse who never travels is at risk. To my knowledge, no research has been done to determine length of immunity, but vaccine manufacturers suggest annual vaccination. Until further information is available, I would suggest an initial sequence of two VEW-T vaccinations at around five and six months of age followed by a booster every three years. If an outbreak occurs in your area, the booster can be given sooner. I would not recommend vaccinating *any* horse over 15 years of age unless there is an outbreak.

West Nile Encephalitis

Because of the current levels of alarm about West Nile, this vaccine cannot be ignored. However, we have to give careful consideration to the effects and effectiveness of this vaccine before giving it. West Nile is not fatal in most cases. It can cause jumpiness, lack of coordination, and some neurological dysfunction. When a patient of mine contracted West Nile (verified through titers), we were able to stop the progression of symptoms within 12 hours and restore the horse to normal health within 48 hours using several homeopathic remedies. I recommend that this vaccine be given once a year at most, and never to horses who are not in good health.

The West Nile vaccine is currently available as a single injection from Merial or in combination with Eastern and Western encephalitis from Fort Dodge. Even though it means giving separate injections, I prefer the Merial vaccine—and hopefully Merial will soon make it available in a combination vaccine. I am not as concerned about giving combination vaccines for several forms of encephalitis at once as I am about giving vaccines for several different diseases at once because the immune response is similar for all forms of encephalitis.

Tetanus

This disease can also cause death if it is not treated early and aggressively. Tetanus is caused by the bacteria clostridium teteni, which generally infects the horse through contamination of a wound. Vaccine manufacturers recommend annual vaccination, but horses have been known to have protection for up to 10 years from a single vaccination. I would suggest the same schedule as encephalitis, with a booster given if your horse sustains an injury and has not been vaccinated within the last year.

Tetanus Antitoxin

This is not a vaccine, but an antitoxin against the tetanus neurotoxin. It should only be given along with tetanus toxoid when the vaccination history is not known and a horse is injured, foaling, going into surgery, or having invasive dental work.

Rabies

Horses can get rabies, and it is fatal. To my knowledge, there are no documented cases of a horse transmitting rabies to a person. To contract rabies, the horse must be bitten by a rabid animal. Wild animals such as skunks, foxes, raccoons, or bats are the usual sources of infection. Vaccine manufacturers recommend an annual rabies vaccination for horses, although the same vaccine is known to provide protection to dogs and cats for at least three years. Although few, there *have* been cases of rabies in vaccinated horses. I do not routinely advise vaccinating for this disease, but if you are concerned and choose to vaccinate, the manufacturer's directions should be followed.

Influenza (Flu)

This is a respiratory disease caused by a virus, and it is rarely fatal. Symptoms include coughing, fever, loss of appetite, and muscle soreness. The virus is acquired from other infected horses. Uncomplicated cases recover in one to three weeks. The best treatment is rest and TLC. Immunity from vaccination is of very short duration, often less than two months, so it is my opinion that vaccination causes more harm than good. Also, horses become less susceptible as they mature. A healthy immune system is the best defense against influenza. In a study with racehorses, there was no difference in infection rates between vaccinated and unvaccinated horses when the horses continued to work. In the same study, vaccinated horses who were taken out of hard training during the outbreak had lower infection rates. Unfortunately, this study did not include unvaccinated horses who were rested. I suspect they would have done just as well. If you choose to give the influenza vaccine, give the intranasal version, which gives year-long immunity rather than just two-month immunity.

Rhinopneumonitis (Rhino)

This viral disease can take several forms. It is an equine herpes virus (there are two types, labeled "1" and "4") and causes mild respiratory infection, primarily in young horses. Infection is acquired from other infected horses. Like influenza, the immunity the horse develops from vaccination can last less than two months, and horses can become latent carriers (with the virus present in the body but not active) of the equine herpes 1 virus. This means the horse stays infected but does not show symptoms or infect other horses unless stressed. Once stressed, however, the horse may or may not show symptoms, but can be a source of infection for other horses. Equine herpes 1 can also cause abortion in pregnant mares. When horses are shipped and congregated together there is more stress on latent carriers. These horses may then become viremic (meaning the virus has become active in the body) and cause abortions in the herd. For this reason, most brood mare farms require that mares be vaccinated for Rhino at five, seven, and nine months of pregnancy. Even this procedure does not always prevent abortion, and yet *some* mares will *not* abort even if they become sick.

Although I prefer to take my chances rather than give these vaccines, you may not have an option if you ship your mare for breeding. If you do not ship your mare, you can use good management to control exposure to the herpes virus. Keep pregnant mares separated from young stock and isolate all horses who have been brought in from other locations for 10 to 14 days before introducing them to the herd.

On rare occasions equine herpes 1 can cause neurological symptoms ranging from mild hind limb incoordination to quadriplegia. I have never seen this from actual infection, but I have often seen pain and persistent hypersensitivity in horses following vaccination. This usually appears about two weeks after the vaccination, and I do not know if the vaccine causes these symptoms directly or perhaps stresses the horse enough to cause a flare up of a latent infection. Despite all the varied disease states this virus can cause, it is rarely fatal with the exception of abortions. I believe that management is the most effective control measure, and that the vaccination may cause more harm than good. Vaccinating for this disease will not provide guaranteed protection. Ohio State University recently had a severe outbreak of the neurological form of herpes in a group of horses who had been routinely vaccinated.

Streptococcus Equi (Strangles)
This is a contagious bacterial infection of the upper respiratory tract that occurs primarily in young horses. It is characterized by inflammation in the nasal passages and throat, a nasal discharge, and abscesses in the regional lymph nodes. It is rarely fatal, although complicated cases do occur. Strangles is usually contracted through contact with infected horses, and this bacteria can live in the environment and become concentrated where large numbers of horses congregate. This strain of strep bacteria can also be transmitted by contamination of inanimate objects such as water or feed buckets. Infected horses may shed this bacteria for several months, which can then infect other horses. Unfortunately, there is no good vaccine for this illness, and I do not recommend vaccination with the current vaccines on the market.

Equine Monocytic Ehrlichiosis (Potomac Horse Fever)
This is a blood-borne disease caused by *ehrlichia risticii*. Clinical symptoms associated with this disease can include severe diarrhea, fever, anemia, leukopenia (low white blood cell count), edema (swelling) of the limbs and lower portions of the body, abortion, colic, and laminitis. Horses can die from this disease, but most recover following appropriate treatment. A study done at Cornell University in 1995 suggested the vaccine for Potomac Horse Fever did not lower rates of infection or severity of disease. I do not recommend vaccination for this disease.

Conclusion
Planning a vaccination program is an important part of horse care. Antibody titers can be measured by taking blood samples and this may help determine your horse's current immune status for diseases such

as encephalitis, influenza, rhinopneumonitis, tetanus, and rabies. After careful consideration of the seven questions at the beginning of this chapter and discussion with your veterinarian, you should be able to determine what is best for you and your horse.

Some Homeopathic Remedies for the Side Effects of Vaccination

There are two major homeopathic remedies that are often recommended for the effects of vaccination: Thuja and Silicea. Here's a brief explanation of both, along with two case studies on the uses of Thuja.

Thuja Occidentalis—Arbor Vitae

This remedy is most often prescribed for the ill effects of vaccination. Its main action is on the skin and genitourinary organs. Symptoms include warts, polyps, lameness in tendons and muscles which is worse in damp weather, rapid exhaustion and emaciation, chronic nasal discharge, chronic diarrhea, distended abdomen, colic, inflamed ovaries, chronic uterine infection, poor quality hooves, and swollen glands.

Thuja Case Studies
Amy: 28-Year-Old Arab Mare

Amy was obtained by her owner in February 1996. She was in very bad shape but was gradually nursed back to health. Her weight, appetite, and hair coat were good, but at a certain point she incurred a puncture wound and needed a tetanus booster. She was accidentally given a combination vaccine containing encephalomyelitis, tetanus, influenza and rhinopneumonitis. The next day she was very depressed and would not eat. Over the next ten days she remained depressed with a poor appetite. She was given one dose of the homeopathic remedy Thuja 200c, which often matches the symptoms caused by the ill effects of vaccination. Although not fully recovered, within 24 hours her attitude and appetite were greatly improved and she was on the mend.

Karisle: Five-Year Old Warmblood Gelding

Karisle had a history of skin eruptions and warts. He had been vaccinated each year for encephalomyelitis, tetanus, influenza, and rhinopneumonitis. After his shots one spring he developed painful papilloma warts in his left ear. He became very head shy and could not be bridled in the normal way. One dose of Thuja 30c was given because it matched his symptom picture. Within two weeks the warts were less obvious and his ear was not as painful. Karisle's tendency toward skin problems and warts suggested that his immune system was weak and future treatment should focus on strengthening his immune system.

Silicea—Pure Flint

Silicea is indicated in ailments secondary to defective nutrition. It will often help with the assimilation of minerals. Poor quality, dry, and cracked hooves are a primary indicator for using Silicea in horses. A tendency toward abscess formation also suggests Silicea. Indicators such as scarring after injury and suffering from the ill effects of vaccination also make Silicea a good choice. It is a deep acting remedy and should be considered for many chronic cases. In addition to the previous symptoms, the horse who needs the constitutional remedy Silicea may be sensitive to heat yet chilly, have swollen glands, and have an excessive dislike for hypodermic injections.

Vaccinations in Boarding Situations

If you try to adhere to holistic and natural care for your horse, getting all your needs met in a boarding situation (especially with regard to vaccinations) can require quite a bit of planning and forethought, not to mention tact and diplomacy!

As a horse owner, you are interested in supporting your horse's immune system with natural methods, and have concerns about the safety and effectiveness of vaccines. You want to use as few vaccines as possible. The stable owner, on the other hand, is concerned about protecting all the horses in the barn using a standard procedure. Most stable owners feel that vaccines are both harmless and effective, and prefer to vaccinate all the horses at once (since this is truly the most effective way to vaccinate). They feel that horse owners who don't want vaccinations are simply trying to save money. Custom vaccination programs can cause complications in recordkeeping, not to mention headaches with the stable's veterinarian.

One solution would be to choose the middle ground. Agree to a minimum of vaccines rather than refusing all of them. Allow vaccinations for the most dangerous diseases, such as encephalitis, tetanus, and rabies. If you have a chronically ill horse or a horse with a poor immune system, ask your own veterinarian to write a letter stating that vaccinations could be harmful to the horse. If the barn owner insists on vaccinating, you have two options: move your horse or get the barn owner to agree to pay for any problems arising from vaccinating your horse (since the labels on vaccines state that they should only be given to healthy animals). It is a rare barn owner who will agree to this, but it does make a point.

Note: Once you've chosen your vaccines, make sure you really get what you want. If you choose to give only tetanus and encephalitis, make sure you're not also getting rhinopneumonitis and/or flu in the same injection. If your veterinarian only carries the combination vaccine for tetanus, encephalitis, rhino, and flu, he may only charge you for the vaccines you requested, but your horse will receive the rhinopneumonitis and flu as well. Make sure you get exactly the vaccinations you ask for and nothing more.

More On the Immune System—Innate Versus Acquired

With so much discussion above on vaccinations and supporting the immune system, it is helpful to discuss briefly the difference between the "innate" and the "acquired" immune system. We are born with the *innate* immune system, which is not specific to any particular organism and is not enhanced by past exposure. It also includes barriers such as the skin and digestive tract, and the mucous barrier in the respiratory system.

The *acquired* immune system is the one we are concerned with when considering vaccines. The acquired immune system includes the lymph nodes, thymus gland, bone marrow, and gut-associated lymph tissue. The acquired immune system is tailored to individual pathogens and enhanced by prior exposure.

The goal of vaccination is to stimulate the acquired immune system so it will produce immunity and protect the horse from future exposure to the organism being vaccinated against. The challenge is to introduce an antigen which will stimulate immunity but not cause disease. The less complex the antigen the easier it is to create a vaccine. Viruses have the least antigenic complexity and are the easiest to create vaccines for. Bacteria are more complex, and parasites are the most complex.

How We Create Vaccines

There are currently three established methods for creating vaccines. New techniques are being sought and developed to make vaccines safer and more effective.

- **Killed Vaccines:** In these vaccines, the virus organisms have been killed so cannot actually create the disease state in the horse. Killed vaccines often contain 10 to 100 times the necessary amount of antigen (the killed virus) needed to stimulate immunity. This is required by law in order to maintain effectiveness over the entire shelf life of the vaccine. These vaccines also require adjuvants, which, as previously discussed, are often toxic themselves. Most equine vaccines are killed virus vaccines. The disadvantage of these is that the combination of large amounts of the killed virus plus toxic adjuvants—*or either of those two factors alone*—can cause adverse reactions.

- **Modified Live Vaccines:** These vaccines actually create a low level of disease in the horse and can cause problems in weak animals. Because the animal does actually become infected, shedding of the virus with modified live vaccines is also a concern because it may infect other horses. In this case the weakened virus is passed to other animals who may develop the disease if they have depressed immune function. Examples of modified live vaccines include Flu Avert intra nasal vaccine from Heska and Rhinomune (EHV-1) from Pfizer. Based on my clinical experience, I do not feel there is an effective vaccine for rhinopneumonitis in horses.

- **Toxoids:** These are chemically altered toxins. Tetanus toxoid is the most common toxoid vaccine in horses. This is a very safe and effective vaccine.

While these three options are the best available to us at this point, research is being done to create safer and more effective vaccines.

Within every population there are animals which are considered low or non-responders. These individuals are genetically unable to build immunity to certain diseases, and vaccination will not be effective for them—they will remain susceptible.

Chapter 7
Parasite Control

Here in Texas we often have very mild winters, which result in a heavy concentration of parasites in the pastures. These circumstances can overpower the immune systems of otherwise healthy horses. No matter what climate you live in, the best way to monitor your horse for parasites is to have routine fecal exams and blood evaluations done by a veterinarian. A fecal egg count helps determine if your horse has adult worms in the digestive tract, however, blood tests are needed to determine if your horse has worms in other areas of the body. Blood evaluations measure your horse's immune response to parasites or, in some cases, can actually detect worms in the blood itself. These tests should be done several times a year and will allow you to evaluate your control program before any problems develop.

Symptoms of Parasite Infestation

To determine whether your horse has parasite infestation, consider these general symptoms:

- General lack of health
- Dull hair coat that doesn't shed
- Weight loss
- Poor hoof condition
- Frequent colic
- Cough or nasal discharge (may indicate roundworm migration)

If your horse exhibits one or more of these symptoms, you may want to examine your deworming program more closely. You'll want to consider how you control parasites, at what intervals you deworm your horse, and the necessity of using a rotational deworming strategy.

Control

Although there are some excellent and safe dewormers on the market, management is still the key to controlling parasites. Horses become infested with strongyles, ascarids and tapeworms by ingesting the eggs or larvae from contaminated pastures and paddocks. The best control is to remove manure promptly and compost it properly before spreading it back on pastures. Another option is to provide very large pastures or rotate pastures so that horses are not forced to graze areas contaminated with manure. This arrangement most closely matches the wild horses' pattern of grazing in one area very heavily then moving on to another area. Despite your best management at home, if you travel to show grounds or rodeos and allow your horse to graze, he may pick up larvae left there by other horses.

Climate must also be considered when designing your deworming program. Parasites are most active in the warmer, humid times of year. This is when you must be most diligent about control. Pasture management combined with regular fecal and blood exams can keep the use of chemical dewormers to a minimum and sometimes eliminate them altogether. It is also important to consider the overall immune system of the horse. A very healthy horse will be resistant to mild parasite burdens. I have been able to go as long as two years without needing to use chemical dewormers on my pasture horses. I gave them a probiotic/ enzyme combination each new and full moon to support normal gut function and detoxification. (It is an old animal husbandry premise that parasites are more active during the full moon. Whether this is true or not, using the new and full moons as worming dates is an easy way to mark the calendar and to remind yourself to stay on a schedule.) The following spring, however, I detected some strongyle eggs on the fecal exam, which I suspected was due to the combination of a mild winter and the introduction of a new horse who might have had a heavy load of encysted small strongyles. Some people report good results feeding diatomaceous earth on a regular basis. This did not work for me, but I could see how it might in a drier climate. N.O.M.S. is another product that, fed daily, may help prevent parasite infestation.

Deworming Intervals

The standard frequency for chemical deworming is every six to eight weeks. This is called "purge deworming" and, depending upon the product used, removes parasites that are in the gut and/or that are migrating through the tissues. Unfortunately there is little if any residual action. In other words, your horse can immediately start picking up new parasites if exposed. This is why products such as StrongidC, which is fed daily, may be your best choice in a highly contaminated environment. Another choice is the natural or herbal dewormers that may decrease the numbers of parasites surviving in the gut. By using these, you may be able to increase the time period between dewormings in cold or very dry conditions. If using a purge deworming plan for foals, start the program when the foals are eight to ten weeks of age. There is some concern that feeding StrongidC on a daily basis to foals may delay onset of acquired immunity to ascarids. Fecal flotation exams or blood evaluations done at two- to four-month intervals allow you to properly evaluate your deworming program, identify horses who are particularly susceptible, and focus your efforts on these horses.

Rotational Deworming

Rotational deworming is the practice of using a different class of dewormer each time you deworm your horse. The small strongyles are the most likely to develop drug resistance. The theory behind rotation of dewormers is that the less the strongyles are exposed to a chemical, the longer it will take them to become resistant to that chemical. In reality this has not proven to be the case. Resistance of small strongyles to normal doses of benzimidole dewormers, at their recommended dosage, is well documented, yet large doses of some drugs in this class are effective against encysted larvae. Your best plan is to work closely with your veterinarian to choose an effective product that has the least toxicity and to deworm at the longest interval possible to maintain minimum but not necessarily zero parasite burden.

Types of Parasites
Strongyles (Blood Worms)

For many years it was thought that the large strongyles were the only real threat to horses' health. The large strongyles cause considerable damage to the blood vessels supplying the intestine during the migration stage. The damage from migrating large strongyles causes many horses to become chronic poor performers or colickers. With the introduction of avermectin-type dewormers that killed migrating large strongyles, the danger of permanent damage to blood vessels was greatly decreased. However, horses continued to colic and do poorly, and it became clear that the small strongyle species are equally damaging, although in a different way.

The small strongyles penetrate the wall of the intestine and become encysted there until conditions become favorable for them to emerge, such as immediately after a purge type deworming when the previous population of small strongyles is cleared from the intestines. The encysted small strongyles then immediately begin to emerge in large numbers. This cycle of small strongyles encysting and emerging creates inflammation and subsequent scarring in the intestinal wall. These encysted larvae are resistant to dewormers, even the avermectins that kill migrating large strongyles. Large and small strongyles are resistant to many dewormers on the market today. My drug of choice is Strongid paste (pyrantel). This is a very safe product that has been on the market for years and has a proven track record. In healthy horses it stays in the digestive tract where it kills the adult worms, and it is not absorbed systemically. Ivermectin, Zimecterin, or Quest (avermectins), on the other hand, are absorbed, which allows them to kill migrating parasites but also increases their toxicity. StrongidC (pyrantel tartrate) is designed to be fed on a daily basis to kill worm larvae as they are ingested and to kill small strongyles as they emerge from the gut wall. Most small strongyles are resistant to benzimidole dewormers such as Panacur (fenbendizole) as a single dose, but may be susceptible to multiple daily doses. Panacur PowerPac is a five-day double dose of fenbendizole, which is effective against encysted small strongyles.

Ascarids (Roundworms)
These worms are rarely a problem in horses over two years old. They can, however, be deadly for youngsters. After the ascarid eggs are ingested, they migrate through the liver and lungs. Many of the "colds" and coughs of babies are actually related to the inflammation in the lungs from roundworm migration. The adult worms can become quite long, and in large numbers cause blockage of the intestine. Roundworms in the intestine are killed by pyrantel, avermectin, and benzimidole dewormers. Avermectins are reported to be effective against adult and migrating ascarids, but based on my experience, I prefer pyrantel or benzimidazoles.

Tapeworms
Tapeworms attach to the intestine at the junction between the small intestine and cecum. This is already a potential area of impaction in the horse, and it is believed by some that tapeworm infestation compounds the problem. Unfortunately, tapeworm eggs do not show up on routine fecal exams, so if regular deworming is not resulting in good health, consider giving pyrantel at two to three times the normal dose. This should kill any tapeworms. Avermectins and benzimidazoles

are not effective against tapeworms at any dosage level, so if you use those they must be combined with praziquantel to provide protection against this parasite.

Oxyuris (Pinworms)

These worms do not cause serious disease but can be irritating to horses. Stabled horses are most at risk. The female worm lays eggs around the anal opening (the peri-anal area), causing the horse to show symptoms of tail rubbing and hair loss. Although these worms are killed by all conventional deworming products, they have a short life cycle and new adults will return in seven to ten days following deworming. Therefore, the best treatment for a horse who is affected is to wash the peri-anal area and surrounding tissues with a mild soap and apply a soothing ointment on a regular basis.

Strongyloides

These worms cause mild diarrhea in babies. Foals become infected via the mare's milk. Benzimidole dewormers are safe and effective to use to treat foals. Control involves removing damp bedding where the worms breed.

Bots

These are not worms at all, but fly larvae. The female botfly, which looks like a bee, lays eggs around the face or legs of the horse. The eggs hatch when exposed to moisture, such as when the horse rubs his eyes, nose, or mouth on his legs. The larvae migrate to the stomach and attach there to develop. The larvae cause little damage, but the flies are extremely irritating to horses. Avermectin-type dewormers are excellent for controlling bots, and treatment is only needed if the small yellow eggs are seen on the legs. Wetting the eggs with warm soapy water or scraping them off the hair is an easy, non-chemical approach to bot control.

Chapter 8
Equine Dentistry

Horses have teeth that are very different from human teeth. Humans have teeth with fixed crowns that are set solidly in the bone. Horses have teeth that actually move or erupt out of the bone as they wear away. Horses in the wild will graze and chew food 12 to 14 hours a day. Your horses will do the same given the opportunity, and this continuous chewing action wears the teeth away, which is what is supposed to happen.

Many years ago people noticed horses having trouble chewing as they aged. Discovering that the horse's teeth were wearing and developing sharp points along the outer edges of the upper molars and along the inner edges of the lower molars, it became evident that something had to be done.

Through domestication, we have doubled the life span of horses, and special care needs to be taken to provide them with a healthy lifestyle. Proper tooth care allows horses to eat more efficiently and actually prolongs the life of the teeth. Since the sharp points that develop cause pain, horses are forced to change the way they chew. This improper chewing can cause many problems. Such imbalance causes irregular wearing patterns on the molars, which brings irregular pressures to be applied to the TMJ, or jaw joint. Now when the horses are trying to chew their food, it also makes their jaw hurt. Proper dental care eliminates all these problems.

By rasping off the sharp edges of the molar arcades (rows of teeth), the horses started eating much better and more efficiently. This process is known as "floating." "Floating," in this context, means to smooth off. Horses have no nerves in the crowns of the teeth, so this process is painless.

Young horses go through several years of changes within the mouth. At around two and a half years, the central incisors shed and the permanent teeth start to erupt. At the same time, the first set of pre-molars do the same thing. At three years the second set of pre-molars shed, and the permanent teeth start to erupt. At three and a half years the second set of incisors shed along with the third set of pre-molars. At four and a half years the third set of incisors shed and the permanent teeth erupt along with the canines on male horses. This is all going on as we put the most pressure on our horses—"training."

Most horses are trained to respond to bit pain. Putting a bit in a young horse's mouth and pulling on the reins presses soft tissue into the sharp points of the first pre-molars. Also, if the wolf teeth haven't been removed, the bit will bang around on them causing more discomfort. This is where most head throwing and behavior problems begin. And we wonder why young horses object to the bit when we start training them! Having horses seen by an equine dentist prior to sending them to the trainer will greatly help the training process.

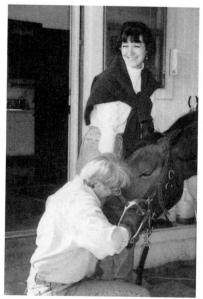

Horse in ideal position for floating.

Performance floating is very important for horses in training and includes special features. For instance, a slight rounding of the first pre-molar of each arcade, top and bottom, sets up what are known as "bit seats." These "seats" allow the horse to wear a bit more comfortably and not experience pain from bit pressure. When this is done, horses become softer and more flexible in the poll. Performance floating young horses prior to training allows the horses to learn to respond to bit *pressure* instead of to bit *pain*. It is equally important, with a good performance float, to pay attention to the molars all the way in the back of the mouth. For proper performance, all teeth need to slide easily across each other forward and backward, as well as side-to-side, which they cannot do if *any* of the molars are neglected. When a performance float is done correctly, the horse is able to flex at the poll up and down and side-to-side without having to open the mouth.

Much advancement has taken place over the years in the field of equine dentistry. New procedures and more sophisticated instruments have improved the types of dental care we can now find for our horses. Along with these improvements comes the attempt at making dentistry easier. Unfortunately, most of these methods are devised to help the practitioner and not the animals. Heavily sedating horses and suspending their heads in an unnatural position is harmful, as is leaving the mouth open for periods longer than 10 or 15 minutes at a time without rest. That being said, power tools can make some dental procedures easier for the horse and dentist. Adjusting molar imbalances such as hooks, ramps, or waved arcades can be done rapidly using proper power instruments. Rotary grinders can accomplish results fast and with minimum or no trauma and with very little sedation. Whether the practitioner uses strictly hand tools, strictly power tools, or a combination of both, when choosing someone to work on your horse's teeth make sure that they have a thorough understanding of the function of the teeth in eating and performance. Also ensure that the person shows compassion for your horse by using minimum sedation and keeping the horse's head in a natural position during the procedure.

In summation, horses need proper, regular dental care. Every horse should have its teeth floated at least once a year, and young performance horses require floating every six months. Along with all the other health care measures we take for our horses, dental care should be considered routine maintenance.

SECTION THREE: DISEASE AND ILLNESS
Chapter 9
Holistic First Aid

Even with the best holistic care, there will still be occasions when health issues arise. These instances usually involve exposure to infectious diseases, injuries, and mild digestive upsets. Knowing how to help your horse in a first aid situation means knowing what's normal for horses. This includes temperature (99-100 degrees), pulse (36-40 beats per minute), and respiration (8-12 breaths per minute). Take these readings on your horse when he is in a healthy state and write them down somewhere so you have them to compare to when you feel he is ailing. You will also need to be able to evaluate the color of the gums (they should be pink, not gray or red), and capillary refill time (this is the time it takes for the gum to turn pink again after you press firmly on it—it should be less than one second). Learn to stop major bleeding with a pressure bandage and keep basic shock remedies on hand.

In addition, increase your powers of observation. Learn what's normal in terms of behavior and appearance for your individual horse. When you're not sure about something, err on the side of caution and let your veterinarian decide whether you can handle the situation by yourself. The more you learn and practice, the more confident you will become in first aid situations.

To get you started, here is a short discussion of holistic first aid, including some of the more common situations you might encounter.

Infectious Disease

The most likely exposure to infectious disease is to respiratory infections from a viral or bacterial cause. With the exception of the intranasal flu vaccine, I do not feel we have good vaccines to prevent these kinds of infections. The intranasal flu vaccine actually stimulates the correct type of immunity because it is administered in the same way natural infection occurs, in the nasal passage. For other types of infectious diseases, your best defense is to build and support the immune system. See the sections on "Nutrition" and "Vaccination" for more details.

If you horse does come down with flu-like symptoms, don't panic. Make notes about his vital signs such as temperature, pulse, respiration, and capillary refill time. Keep him in a quiet place and don't stress him. Support his immune system and stimulate his appetite by giving him a probiotic paste. Don't worry about temperatures in the 104-105 degree range if your horse's vital signs are good. Also, don't worry too much if your horse backs off his feed. You *do* want to make sure your horse is drinking because fever can lead to dehydration. Dehydration is a concern, especially with persistent fever, so in that case consider warm bran mashes with moist treats like apples and carrots to encourage water consumption. Only if your horse is severely depressed, or you know he's dehydrated, do you want to lower his temperature with medication. Fever is the body's way of making it hard for infective agents to live and reproduce, and fasting allows the body to focus energy on the immune response. Giving a nutrient dense food such as blue-green algae provides support to the immune system without requiring energy for digestion.

Antioxidants such as vitamin C or noni juice can be very helpful in healing the inflammation created by this type of infection. Natural immune stimulants such as echinacea, beta glucan, and colostrum can be used as well. Homeopathy can be very good for acute infections. It is important to look at your horse's symptoms and carefully select the best remedy. For instance, a dry hacking cough would call for a different remedy than a moist one. Get help from your holistic veterinarian if necessary.

If your horse has contracted a streptococcal bacterial infection you may have to deal with abscesses in the lymphatic glands. Warm compresses and drawing agents such as Epsom salts can speed the maturation and draining of the abscess. Never attempt to open an abscess unless you can see a clear area where the tissue has thinned. Lancing an abscess before it has matured can slow the healing process and cause your horse unnecessary discomfort. Consider consulting with a homeopathic veterinarian if your horse does not seem to be recovering well. Echinacea is very useful for fighting the bacteria without slowing the immune response and can be used for up to two to three weeks at a time. Some of these cases can be stubborn, but antibiotics should always be your last resort. Antibiotics will slow the maturation of abscesses and in some cases lead to internal abscesses that can be life threatening.

Acute Laminitis

Laminitis, or inflammation of the equine foot, should always be treated as an emergency, and there are some important steps you can take as you wait for your veterinarian to arrive. Laminitis can have many causes including but not limited to an overload of grain or other rich feed or forage, systemic infections, excessive hoof concussion from working on hard ground, reactions to drugs or vaccines, digestive upsets, or injury to the opposite leg which causes extra weight bearing on the unaffected one.

Common symptoms of laminitis include:

- A stiff gait or unwillingness to move.

- A shifting of the weight to the hind legs.

- Rapid breathing and a strong digital (foot) pulse. The pulse may be strong enough to be seen by looking closely at the blood vessels as they pass down the inside and outside of the lower legs. The pulse can be checked by feeling for it at the level of the fetlock or mid-pastern area.

- Heat in the hoof.

Treatment of Acute Laminitis

Digital pulse points in a laminitic horse.

If your horse is in a lot of pain he is not going to want to move, but it is still important to get him to a place with soft ground or bedding. To help him move more comfortably you can tape a support under his frog on each affected foot. These supports can be made from rolled up gauze or hard rubber. These supports should not extend outside the borders of the frog. You can also tape styrofoam blocks under the entire foot. These blocks will compress under the weight of the horse, so can be placed under the whole hoof without concern of their interfering with the circulation of the blood to the coffin bone.

Once you have your horse on soft ground, soak the affected feet in ice water to combat the inflammation and minimize damage. These ice water soaks should be continued if possible until your horse is able to walk without severe pain. If your horse will not tolerate the soaks, wrap his feet in a 50/50 mix of Draw solution and water and keep the bandages wet with it until the pain decreases.

Homeopathy can be very valuable in acute laminitis and there are several remedies to consider:

- ***Belladonna:*** There may be a pounding pulse, dilated pupils, and heat in the feet. I give either a 200c or a 1m potency one to three times a day.

- ***Aconite:*** Similar to Belladonna but the horse is more frantic and fearful. Again, I use 200c–1m one to three times a day.

- ***Arnica:*** These horses are much less dramatic. They mainly act stiff and sore with an elevated but not pounding digital pulse. Again, 200c–1m one to three times daily.

- ***Apis:*** There is extreme swelling of the lower legs. These horses are thirstless and worse from heat. I give either a 30c or 200c potency one to three times a day.

- ***Nux Vomica:*** I use Nux when symptoms develop after overeating green grass, feed or heavily fertilized hay. I give a 30c potency once an hour for four doses.

I do not recommend using non-steroidal anti-inflammatory drugs once the symptoms of laminitis are obvious. At this point damage has already occurred in the internal structures of the hoof, and I would prefer to have the horse's natural pain response present in order to limit his movement and prevent further damage to the lamina. In my experience, giving these drugs will cause the horse to look better for the short term but suffer more serious damage long term. Instead I suggest high levels of natural antioxidants such as coenzyme Q10, Cell Tech Super Sprouts and Algae, MSM, or noni juice. These antioxidants cannot undo the original inflammation but will prevent additional damage without masking pain. Another potent antioxidant is DMSO, and your veterinarian may want to administer this product in an intravenous injection. I feel this approach is a better alternative than non-steroidal anti-inflammatory drugs in severe cases of acute laminitis.

If your horse is healthy going into an acute case of laminitis he has a very good chance of a full recovery.

Colic
Impaction Colic

This is the most common form of colic in horses. It can usually be resolved if treated early, but can become life threatening if poorly managed. To understand why horses are so prone to impaction colic one only needs to look at the anatomy of their digestive tract. The large colon of the horse measures 10 to 13 feet long with an average volume of 21 gallons. It lays in the abdomen in the shape of a double U by running forward from the right side (right ventral colon), bending double at the diaphragm and continuing back on the left side (left ventral colon). At the pelvis it makes another U-turn and goes forward again (left dorsal colon) then bends again at the diaphragm to go down the right side (right dorsal colon). As if all of this bending around wasn't enough, at the pelvic flexure the left dorsal colon becomes much narrower. It is no surprise that this area is the most common site of impactions. Another common site of impaction is the part of the large intestine called the "small colon," or the "descending colon." This narrow section reaches a length of up to 13 feet and is located mostly on the left side of the abdomen.

Symptoms of Impaction Colic

Horses with uncomplicated impaction colic are usually not in severe pain. They may refuse food and water, look around at their sides, paw the ground, and lie down. They may have intermittent cramping but are rarely in sustained, severe discomfort. Mild dehydration may show up as dry gums and skin that is less flexible than normal. Impactions usually develop over several hours or days, so it is important to check the stall for manure. If there has been no manure in over 12 hours it may indicate a more advanced case. This is important to determine because some horses have a high pain tolerance and won't exhibit discomfort until the impaction is well established. Also, horses with this kind of colic may cut back on their water consumption. This should be an early warning sign, even if the horse appears fine otherwise.

Treatment of Impaction Colic

Even if symptoms are mild it is still a good idea to get in touch with your veterinarian. Most impactions do not require immediate attention, but if your horse does not respond to your first aid it is good to get on your veterinarian's schedule. After noting vital signs such as pulse, temperature, respiration, gum color, gut motility, and degree of pain, take your horse out for a short five- to ten-minute walk. Sometimes this is all it takes for a stalled horse to get a mild impaction moving. TTeam bodywork, ear work, and belly lifts may help relax your horse. The homeopathic remedy Nux vomica will often help increase intestinal motility. I use a 6c potency given once every ten minutes for up to four doses. If your horse seems to be having some cramping, you can alternate Nux vomica and Chamomile 30c. You can also give a probiotic paste which will increase motility by replenishing beneficial bacteria in the gut.

If these measures do not bring relief to your horse within one hour it is a good idea to proceed to conventional veterinary treatment. Mineral oil and oral electrolytes are my first line treatments for impaction colic. After a physical exam, a stomach tube is passed to remove any gas from the stomach and to administer the medications. One-half to one gallon of mineral oil will lubricate the impaction, and one-half to one gallon of oral electrolytes will correct mild dehydration. If pain is not relieved by removing gas from the stomach, then an anti-inflammatory agent such as Banamine can be given. Removing the gas from the stomach is critical before giving any pain reliever. Most horses cannot burp, so covering up pain from a distended stomach with drugs could lead to serious consequences.

Once a horse has received a pain killer he should be observed for at least five hours to make sure he is still pain free after the drug is out of his system. Grain and hay should be withheld until oil is passing in the manure. This usually takes 12-24 hours. Bran mashes and grass can be offered, in moderation, if your horse is hungry. If your horse is not drinking consider adding one teaspoon of Lite Salt to the bran mash. Nux vomica 30c can be given twice a day to encourage your horse to drink following impaction colic.

Acupuncture can also be valuable for a stubborn case of impaction colic. If gut motility does not return, your horse may still be dehydrated. If oral fluids are not enough, intravenous fluids may be required. Do not hesitate to go this route if your veterinarian recommends it.

Prevention of Impaction Colic
Exercise and good dental care are the best preventions for impaction colic. Also make sure that fresh clean water is available at all times. My rule is that if your horse doesn't drink he doesn't get to eat. In other

words, if you see a decrease in water consumption, immediately increase the level of exercise and decrease the amount food. Give probiotics and a bran mash to avoid problems. The same rule holds if you see a decline in the amount of manure being passed. A good deworming schedule is also important. Some horses prone to impaction colic will do better on alfalfa or a grass/alfalfa hay mix.

Spasmodic and Gas Colic

I am discussing these two types of colic together because they have similar causes and presenting symptoms. Improper digestion from various causes is responsible for these colics. Stress from nervousness, weather changes, feed changes, and overwork can result in spasmodic or gas colic. To explain why the horse is so sensitive we must again look at the anatomy and physiology of the digestive tract. The horse is designed to graze continually throughout the day and to eat mostly roughage such as grass. Because fiber is digested in the lower intestine, or colon, this organ has the capacity to hold lots of food. In contrast, the stomach, which under natural grazing conditions would rarely hold much food at a time, is very small. The maximum capacity of the stomach of the average horse is only two to three gallons. The small intestine is 75 feet long but only about two to three inches in diameter. Because most horses cannot vomit or burp, they develop problems quickly if food does not move to the large intestine before fermentation begins. Digestion of starches and fats occurs in the stomach and small intestine so foods high in sugars are more likely to begin fermentation in this area and cause gas.

Symptoms of Spasmodic and Gas Colic

Remember, impaction colics generally come on slowly with low-level discomfort. The opposite is true with spasmodic and gas colics. Your horse can act normal one minute then experience a lot of pain the next. These horses often lie down and roll violently with little regard for their safety or that of their handlers. They may sweat and breathe very rapidly. The pulse and gum color are generally normal in uncomplicated cases. The manure may be loose, and in the case of gas colic your horse will appear bloated. With spasmodic colic your horse may seem to relax, experience pain for a few minutes, and then relax again. These colics often occur around or shortly after feeding.

Treatment of Spasmodic and Gas Colic

The main goal should be to get your horse to relax so he can begin digesting properly. These colics can often resolve as quickly as they appear if you act promptly. Carefully halter your horse and get him into a safe area where you can walk him around. This will often settle him down and give you time to examine him. If his gum color is abnormal (anything other than pink), his pulse is over 40, or he looks bloated, call your veterinarian immediately. If the walking seems to relax him you can give a dose of probiotics to stimulate his digestion. You can also give the homeopathic remedy Chamomile 30c orally every five to ten minutes for four doses. This should help calm the spasms and help your horse relax more. Neither of these treatments will mask any symptoms. If your horse is still uncomfortable after 20 to 30 minutes, call your veterinarian and get on the schedule. The colic may still resolve on its own, but it is better to play it safe.

Your veterinarian will probably want to administer a mild sedative and painkiller and pass a stomach tube. This is a good idea to remove any gas or fluid from the stomach. Fluid reflux from the stomach can indicate a more serious indigestion problem or inflammation. Mineral oil is often given to prevent gas formation. Oral electrolytes may or may not be needed, as dehydration is not as often a problem in these colics as it is in impactions, and it is important not to overload an already full stomach. Once the pain is relieved it is best to put your horse into an environment where he will be most relaxed. If your horse is still suffering from excess gas, you can give the homeopathic remedy Colchicum 30c every five to ten minutes for four doses. If your horse is comfortable and passing manure, you can offer a small amount of hay or grass as soon as the pain medication wears off. Try to determine the cause of the colic and change your management if such is indicated and you are able to do so.

Prevention of Spasmodic and Gas Colic

It is important to maintain horses in as natural an environment as possible. If you cannot offer them access to pasture, at least give them plenty of grass hay to munch on. Keep the grain meals small (no more than two gallons at a time) and feed them more frequently if your horse is a hard keeper. You can also increase the fat in the diet or add alfalfa hay to help your horse gain or maintain weight without increasing the grain portion of his diet. Check your horse for internal parasites and have his teeth examined at least once a year.

Regular exercise is important but be careful not to feed your horse if he is overheated. Your horse can overheat even while standing in his pen or stall on a very hot day, so delay the grain portion of the diet until the sun goes down and the temperature drops. If this is not possible, consider giving only a small portion of his grain or a bran mash. If you suspect your horse is overheated, hosing him down with cool water will help lower his body temperature. If your horse is under stress that you cannot control, feed him probiotics on a daily basis. Also consider adding probiotics as a cautionary measure if you suspect your horse will be stressed in any given situation, such as at a horse show or when being shipped.

Injuries
Bruises

Bruises or hematomas are probably the most common horse injury. Kicks from other horses are usually the cause. Hematomas are formed from ruptured blood vessels under the skin. The blood accumulates in pockets and creates a soft, fluid-filled swelling. The first thing to do is confine your horse so he does not move around and cause additional bleeding into the tissue at the site of the injury. Resist the temptation to give anti-inflammatory drugs such as Banamine or Bute, as these drugs have an anticoagulant effect. Cold water hosing or ice packs will do more to stop the bleeding and associated pain.

Give the homeopathic remedy Arnica as soon as possible. Ideally you should give one or two doses right away of a higher potency, such as a 1m or 10m. Two to three doses per day for one to three days may be indicated when the injury is severe. When I was practicing strictly conventional medicine, I would always drain the serum off these hematomas after about ten days. I have not had to do this even once in the ten years since I have been using Arnica in this way. With the Arnica, I find the blood tends to form a clot faster, and the resulting serum is reabsorbed back into the body at a faster rate. As a bonus, Arnica also is a very effective pain reliever and brings much relief to an injured horse.

For this type of injury you should keep your horse quiet for about ten days, and then you should be able to resume exercising him. If at any time the hematoma looks larger, repeat the Arnica. It is not uncommon to have a hard swelling remain for quite some time in the area of the injury. After all the serum has been reabsorbed it is safe to apply medications to stimulate circulation into the area, such as DMSO or an herbal liniment like Formula 11 or Sore No More. This will help the body break down the scar tissue remaining from the injury.

Minor Cuts and Abrasions

Minor cuts and abrasions are common, especially on the lower legs of horses. After hosing and cleaning off the dirt, I like to wrap these wounds with a cotton bandage soaked in Draw solution mixed in a 50/50 dilution with water, and then apply a standing bandage. I avoid soaps and antiseptics unless the wound is severely contaminated. The Draw solution keeps the swelling down and helps with soreness. The bandage supports the tissues in the lower legs to keep down the swelling. This bandage should be changed once or twice a day for several days. After the initial inflammation has subsided, the bandaging can be discontinued, and the Draw solution can be sprayed on the leg several times a day as needed to keep the swelling down and promote healing. Arnica can be used in these cases but will often not have as dramatic an effect as it does with injuries to the muscles. I will definitely use it, however, if there is lameness.

Stone Bruises

Stone bruises are more common in horses that are kept in stalls and are not ridden regularly on rough ground. They can also occur in pastured horses when the weather has been wet for a long time then turns dry. The horse's sole may not be able to toughen up and develop a callous fast enough to withstand the dry rough ground. Homeopathic Arnica given internally can promote re-absorption of serum so that the bruise is less likely to turn into an abscess. Homeopathic Hypericum can be helpful for bruises that are extremely painful. In addition to the oral homeopathic forms of Arnica and Hypericum, tinctures of both can also be applied topically. (Tinctures are herbal extracts preserved in grain alcohol.) I dilute ten drops of tincture in one ounce of water and apply it under a bandage. Soaking in a hot Epsom salts solution can draw the soreness out of bruised hooves. Durasole or a similar sole toughening product can be applied several times a week to dry the sole out in wet weather. Be careful not to get these products on the frog or skin.

Hoof Abscesses

Hoof abscesses can and often do occur after deep bruises or following puncture wounds. A drawing product such as ichthammol can be applied under a bandage to encourage the abscess to come to the surface. A clay poultice is also a good idea if the hoof is dry and hard. The poultice will soften the hoof wall and may thereby relieve pain by allowing it to expand. It is not a good idea to leave the poultice on for more than 24 hours. Hoof testers can be used to locate the abscess and a farrier or veterinarian can use a hoof knife to open up an area to allow for easier drainage. It is best to remove only as much hoof as needed, because removing too much allows tissue to prolapse or protrude, and this can delay healing. Once the abscess has been opened, the foot can be soaked daily in Epsom salts solution to draw out the infection and allow healing from the inside out. Some horses are reluctant to put their feet in buckets, so as an alternative you can put about one tablespoon of Epsom salts in a disposable diaper, add about one-half cup of water, and bandage this onto the foot. Then cover it all with some kind of plastic bag, such as a heavy duty freezer bag, and wrap it securely with Vetwrap and/or duct tape. This wrap can be replaced every 12 to 24 hours until the bandage consistently comes off clean. A dry bandage can then be used until the abscess is healed.

I do not use antibiotics for hoof abscesses. The very fact that an abscess has formed suggests the body has walled off the problem. Systemic antibiotics, therefore, just weaken the immune response. I also avoid anti-inflammatory drugs, as the inflammation is part of the healing process. Stopping the inflammation will slow the maturation of the abscess and prolong the time it takes to open and drain. Immune support products such as colostrum or beta glucan can be used. Homeopathy can be used, but one must first determine which remedy best fits the case. Abscesses which are extremely painful may respond to a homeopathic remedy called Hepar sulph. Localized, less painful abscesses often do well with Silicea, and deep diffuse abscesses may require Sulphur.

Homeopathy and First Aid

Advantages of Homeopathy in First Aid	Disadvantages of Homeopathy in First Aid
• No side effects • Will not mask symptoms • Given orally, no injections • Stimulates and strengthens animal's immune system • Inexpensive	• No action if remedy is not selected carefully • Response may be less dramatic than conventional medicine • Action is very specific so several remedies may have to be tried before response is seen

Methods for Administering Homeopathic Remedies

Homeopathic remedies are given internally in extremely small doses. Samuel Hahnemann discovered that by putting the remedy through a series of dilutions and agitations he was able to make it more potent in action each time; therefore, the diluted medicine is said to be in a potency.

A commonly used potency is 30c: the original substance has been diluted one drop to 100 drops of water and agitated; then one drop of this mixture is diluted in 100 more drops of water. This process continues 30 times. The final solution is infused into small sugar pellets which are taken orally. When giving homeopathic remedies to horses, I usually dissolve four or five pellets in a clean syringe filled with spring or distilled water and squirt it into the horse's mouth. Most horses take the medicine very willingly. The medicine is absorbed by the mucous membranes and does not need to be swallowed.

In severe, acute conditions, the remedies can be given every 15 minutes for up to four doses, or until a response is seen. Less severe or acute conditions require less frequent dosage, anywhere from one to 24 hours apart. If four doses of the remedy have not brought a response, then it is probably not going to act because it is probably not the correct remedy for that set of symptoms. In any case, the medication is discontinued as soon as the animal is obviously moving toward recovery.

Homeopathic First Aid Kit

- Stethoscope
- Ace bandage or polo wrap
- Thermometer
- Telfa pads
- Scissors
- Duct tape
- Large gauze pads
- Medium-sized syringes, a separate one for each remedy (a 12cc size is best)
- Quilt leg wrap

Homeopathic Remedies
Core Remedies

These are the remedies and their potencies I use most frequently for first aid treatment with horses.

- Aconite 1m
- Apis 200c
- Arnica 1m and ointment
- Arsenicum 30c
- Calendula ointment
- Chamomilla 30c
- Colchicum 30c
- Hyper/cal tincture
- Hypericum 1m and tincture
- Nux vomica 6c
- Pulsatilla 200c
- Silicea 30c

Additional Remedies for Specific Conditions such as Laminitis or Hoof Abscesses

- Belladonna 30c
- Hepar sulph 30c
- Sulphur 30c
- Thuja 1m

Indication for Use of Core Remedies
Aconite—Monkshood

This remedy is made from a beautiful but poisonous plant that grows on the mountains of France, Switzerland, and Germany. The primary indication for Aconite is acute, violent fever and inflammation. Aconite would not be considered after pathological changes have occurred. Acute influenza is a classic Aconite condition. Complaints often come on after exposure to dry cold weather, but extreme heat may also bring on symptoms. The mental state is one of fear and anguish. This remedy is excellent for horses that panic when asked to perform such tasks as trailer loading, clipping, or entering a show ring. Aconite would not be the choice for the horse that doesn't do these things just because he doesn't want to.

Apis—Honeybee
The typical reaction to a bee sting gives the picture of Apis. Swelling, edema, soreness, intolerance of heat and the slightest touch are classic Apis symptoms. Apis is most often used for allergic reactions with puffy-type swelling. It can be life saving in an acute anaphylactic shock-type reaction. Another use for Apis would be joint swelling with heat, excessive fluid, and pain. In mares, Apis may be used for ovarian inflammation and cyst formation, especially when on the right side. Apis patients lack thirst in most cases, but may occasionally show extreme thirst.

Arnica—Leopard's Bane
Arnica is a flowering herb that is routinely used by herbalists and homeopaths. It is applied topically in tincture form for injuries, but homeopathic preparation allows its internal use. Arnica is a remedy that no household should be without. It is used primarily for muscle soreness and bruises. It should be the first remedy given for all injuries, then other remedies may follow, based on the individual's healing response. Arnica should also be considered for any symptoms that develop post-injury. Head injuries are notorious for causing persistent symptoms long after the original injury appears to be healed. Septic conditions may also respond to Arnica.

Arsenicum—Arsenic Trioxide
This extremely toxic chemical is a powerful homeopathic remedy. Consistent with homeopathic principle, it is used for treatment of symptoms that Arsenic would cause if ingested in crude form. For one, it is used to treat food poisoning (i.e., garbage gut in dogs, moldy feed enteritis in horses). General symptoms that would indicate Arsenicum

include restlessness with extreme exhaustion, bloody diarrhea and vomiting, and putrid discharges. Any discharges in Arsenicum cases are thin and irritating. The patient is usually very thirsty, but only for frequent small drinks.

Arsenicum is a very deep acting remedy with many indications in all animals. It is a good remedy to learn in depth for treating chronic diseases. It should be considered for any patient that is restless, fearful, thirsty, and chilly.

Calendula—Marigold
This remedy can be used internally but is more commonly applied externally in lotion, gel, or ointment form to open wounds. It is excellent for speeding the healing of wounds and for repelling insects from wounds.

Chamomilla—Chamomile
Another favorite of herbalists and homeopaths, Chamomilla is most famous for its calming effects. It is often called the "teething baby remedy." Mothers depend on Chamomilla to relieve not only teething, but also earache and colic pains in children. In horses Chamomilla is primarily a colic remedy, but it also seems to be helpful in stressful situations like trailering, especially where the horse's actions would indicate that he might experience motion sickness or nausea from stress. Spasmodic, cramping pains are typical. Animals who are overly sensitive to pain will be most likely to respond well to Chamomilla. Mental calmness contra-indicates Chamomilla. It may also be helpful before any anxiety-producing event.

Colchicum—Meadow Saffron
Another toxic plant with medicinal properties, Colchicum is primarily used for joint stiffness. It is also an excellent remedy for colic in horses. These horses will be very bloated with high-pitched gas sounds heard when listening over either flank. It is best used in conjunction with Nux vomica, as many gas colic cases also have an impaction in the intestine. In these types of colics, the horses may pass a small amount of manure covered with mucous.

Hypericum—St. John's Wort
Another popular herb, Hypericum is a great remedy for injuries to

nerves, especially of the fingers, toes, teeth, and hooves. Excessive pain is a symptom of injuries calling for Hypericum. It can help prevent tetanus after puncture wounds. It can also be used for pain after surgical operations. It is excellent for injuries to the spine, so is good for dogs and cats who get their tails caught in doors or horses who sit back and fall on the base of their tails. Hypericum should also be considered for animal bites and laceration wounds with accompanying weakness from loss of blood. It is an excellent toothache remedy. Externally, Hypericum is often used in tincture form, which we have described previously, to ease the pain of damaged nerves, for instance after a nail puncture in the hoof.

Nux Vomica—Poison Nut
This poisonous substance in crude form creates in the patient oversensitivity to external impressions. The patient reacts violently to light, sound, or odors. The Nux vomica type may also react negatively to drugs. Nux is frequently used by homeopaths to start cases that have been heavily medicated. Many skin conditions respond well to Nux vomica initially, but other remedies may be needed to finish the case. Spasms and constrictions are typical of Nux, which makes it a good choice for cystitis in cats. Nux vomica is a good remedy for impaction colic in horses. These colic cases are not as painful as those needing Chamomilla. It is very important not to forget the mental state when treating something like colic. For example, the Aconite case may be in a state of anguish, the Chamomilla case is irritable, and the Nux patient is downright mean. Overeating and lack of exercise are often in the history of the Nux patient. Nux is especially useful for show horses on high grain rations who spend extended periods of time confined to their stall.

Pulsatilla—Wind Flower
Pulsatilla is primarily a female remedy. As a general rule these patients have a wonderful and gentle disposition. They love attention, and cat owners especially will report how affectionate they are. However, Pulsatilla can have its peevish side, particularly mares who change their personalities dramatically when they come in heat. Pulsatilla is a great remedy for abscesses in all animals and summer colds in horses. Discharge is thick, bland, and yellowish green. Pulsatilla patients usually dislike heat, lack thirst, and prefer to be outdoors.

Silicea—Pure Flint

Silicea is indicated in ailments secondary to defective nutrition and will often help with the assimilation of minerals. Poor quality, dry, cracked hooves are a primary indicator in horses. A tendency toward abscess formation also suggests Silicea. Scarring after injury and ill effects of vaccination also make Silicea a good choice. This is a deep acting remedy and should be considered for many chronic cases. In addition to the previous symptoms, the Silicea type may be sensitive to heat yet chilly, have swollen glands, and have an excessive dislike for hypodermic injections.

Indications for Use of Additional Remedies
Belladonna—Deadly Nightshade

I use this remedy much less often than Aconite. However, in acute laminitis it may be indicated in a horse with a pounding digital pulse who does not appear overly anxious. Horses with high fevers who appear to be in a trance-like state may also respond well to this remedy.

Hepar Sulph—Calcium Sulphide

With a hoof abscess, Silicea is generally the first remedy to use, and most abscesses respond well to it. However, if the abscess is extremely painful and the horse violently resists examination, Hepar sulph may be a better choice.

Sulphur

If all indications point toward a hoof abscess but there is no sign of it on the hoof exterior, then you may have a deep abscess that would respond best to Sulphur. These deep abscesses can often take as long as two or three months to resolve, which differentiates them from the Silicea or Hepar sulph type of abscess.

Thuja

This remedy is indicated for the ill effects of vaccines. Symptoms include a dull hair coat, poor quality hooves, susceptibility to skin infections, warts, and sarcoids.

Chapter 10
Common Chronic Conditions

Like people, horses are subject to a host of common chronic conditions that can range from mildly irritating to performance inhibiting. Luckily, most of these conditions can be treated holistically. In this section I specifically address the holistic treatment of the following common conditions:

- Stocking Up
- Colds and Respiratory Infections
- Chronic Obstructive Pulmonary Disease (COPD or Heaves)
- Skin Conditions
- Uveitis
- Anhydrosis
- Leaky Gut Syndrome
- Laminitis

Stocking Up

There are several reasons for horses to get swelling in the lower legs (stocking up). The most common is poor lymphatic drainage. Unlike blood circulation, which depends on the pumping action of the heart, lymphatic circulation depends on body movement. The contracting and relaxing of muscles pushes the lymphatic fluid through its network of vessels. Within the lymphatic vessels are one-way valves which prevent the lymph from moving in the wrong direction. When there is limited movement, as when a horse is standing for long periods in a stall, the lymph is not being moved and will settle in the lower limbs.

In most cases, a few minutes of exercise will get the lymph fluid moving and the swelling will resolve. If the swelling does not go down with exercise it may mean the valves or gates within the lymphatic vessels are not closing properly. In this case applying leg wraps with some pressure and then exercising your horse should solve the problem. You can repeat the process of wrapping and exercising several times to get the swelling down totally.

Horses don't always stock up when their movement is limited, which in part has to do with the character of the lymphatic fluid. The purpose of lymphatic circulation is to carry toxins away from the tissues. The more toxins in the lymphatic fluid, the thicker it becomes and the harder it is to move. Feeding your horse the best quality nutrients and avoiding drugs and other chemicals will put less stress on the lymphatic system by minimizing toxins in body tissues. High chlorophyll foods like fresh grass and blue-green algae help the body detoxify. With fewer toxins to carry, lymphatic circulation improves.

Standing wraps can be applied when horses are stalled to prevent stocking up, but if this has to be done routinely then it is a palliative treatment and does not address the underlying problem. It may be beneficial to apply standing wraps after hard exercise because the free radicals generated in the body following the exercise may cause tissue damage and subsequent swelling in the lower legs. Support wraps on the lower legs prevent the lymphatic circulation from being overwhelmed by the extra demand. Also, feeding extra antioxidants such as blue-green algae, MSM, and noni juice can help deactivate the free radicals formed after heavy exercise.

Occasionally swelling of the lower legs will occur due to poor blood circulation from a weak heart or electrolyte imbalances due to kidney weakness. Nutritional support including balancing electrolytes and lowering the protein in the diet may then be effective. Homeopathy, acupuncture, or chiropractic can support better organ function. If the problem persists, a good Western medicine diagnostic workup would be indicated to determine the underlying cause of the problem.

Colds and Respiratory Infections

It is very common for young horses to develop coughs and nasal discharge. This is a natural process, as the horse is building his immune system. Sometimes these symptoms can persist because the young growing horse has multiple stresses on his system at the same time. For instance, because he has been weaned from his mother he has to find his place in the herd. Also, rapid growth, parasites, vaccinations, and training programs can interfere with his immune system's development. Further damage can be done if antibiotics are used for low-grade infections rather than allowing the horse's own immune system to fight off the infection. In some cases antibiotics can cause the nasal discharge to clear temporarily only to return when they are stopped. Alternately, the discharge can disappear altogether but be replaced by a deeper infection in the bronchial or lung tissue. If an upper respiratory infection has been suppressed with antibiotics, chronic coughing and exercise intolerance may suggest a deeper infection.

The best treatments for chronic colds and respiratory infections include:

- Cutting back on or stopping training.

- Clearing intestinal parasites. Ascarids (roundworms) migrate through the lungs and create inflammation.

- Increasing nutritional support with probiotics, whole food vitamin and mineral supplements, and antioxidants such as vitamins C and E, noni juice, and blue-green algae.

- Adding extra immune system supporters such as ImmuSun (beta glucan) or Transfer Factors (colostrum derived), although these will be beneficial only if the nutritional needs of the horse have first been met.

In some cases young horses can develop chronic inflammation of the lymphoid tissues in the back of the throat. If this happens it may take weeks or months for full healing to occur. Continuing these horses in training will only prolong the healing time. Rest, good nutrition, and natural antioxidants will allow these horses to recover more quickly.

Older horses with fully developed immune systems are less likely to get frequent upper respiratory infections. If an older horse does develop a respiratory infection, it is likely to be short-term and self-limiting. Any chronic cough or nasal discharge in an older horse should be investigated with an endoscopic examination to check for sinus or guttural pouch infection. In the case of a chronic cough, with or without nasal discharge, a tracheal wash or bronchoalveolar lavage (BAL) can also be done to check for infection or chronic inflammation in the lungs.

Chronic Obstructive Pulmonary Disease (COPD or Heaves)

Heaves is an inflammatory condition that affects the small airways in the lungs and can cause bronchospasms and bronchial hyperirritability. In the acute phase of this condition, the horse develops mucous plugs, while in chronic cases the horse suffers from pathology and eventual obstruction of the airways. Dust, molds, and pollens can all contribute to the development of heaves. Drugs such as steroids, bronchodilators, or expectorants can give immediate short-term relief of symptoms, but only management changes can relieve symptoms long term and prevent permanent damage to the lungs. Any chronic cough, especially accompanied by exercise intolerance, should be investigated to rule out heaves.

If your horse has developed heaves, you must determine what conditions make the heaves worse before you can take the necessary steps to prevent the progression of symptoms. Allergies to dust and mold spores in hay tend to be worse in dry windy weather. Other mold allergies are worse when the horse is kept in the barn on shavings or straw bedding. Horses that are worse when kept in pasture but better in the barn or during certain seasons probably have allergies to pollens. Once you determine what triggers your horse's symptoms, you must change your management program to keep your horse away from those environmental conditions at all costs. Even bringing your horse into the barn for grooming or shoeing can trigger an attack.

In addition to providing clean and non-dusty feeds, soaking hay to remove pollen and dust, and providing a mold-free environment, you can support your horse's health by adding probiotics, whole food supplements, and antioxidants to his diet. Probiotics help thin the mucous in the airways and antioxidants help decrease inflammation. Do not vaccinate these horses, as this could trigger more symptoms and further weaken the immune system. Homeopathy, acupuncture, or bodywork can help control symptoms and help your horse feel better, but these modalities are not likely to cure a horse with severe symptoms.

Skin Conditions

As I travel around to different barns, I am amazed at how many horses have skin problems. Most of these horses receive excellent care and are very healthy, with the exception being their skin condition. Because the skin, along with the liver and kidneys, is a very important organ for detoxification, it is very crucial not to suppress skin eruptions and thereby take away this line of defense from the body. Skin conditions can have a variety of causes, including but not limited to poor nutrition, allergic reactions, insect bites, toxicity, and individual constitutional characteristics. Most of these conditions can be addressed with nutritional therapy, management, topical applications, and constitutional treatment using modalities such as (but not limited to) acupuncture and homeopathy. Finding the underlying cause of the condition is the best way to determine a course of treatment.

Damp Skin Conditions

Some types of horses are badly affected by dampness. These horses tend to have weepy skin lesions such as scratches. They are prone to thrush and white line disease in the hooves, and are also susceptible to viral, bacterial, fungal, and yeast infections. Hives that appear as fluid-filled welts under the skin would be another example of a "damp" skin condition. Many damp skin conditions can be traced to disturbances in the digestive system (see section on Leaky Gut Syndrome).

Treatment for Damp Skin Conditions

- **Diet:** Keep the diet as simple as possible. Additives such as sugars and artificial preservatives, flavorings, and colorings contribute to dampness. Excessive amounts of fat, especially animal fat, will also cause dampness. Foods which dry out dampness are corn, alfalfa, herbs such as chaparral and chamomile, and blue-green algae. Oats do not directly decrease dampness but they are good because they support the spleen/pancreas. Flax seed oil is high in omega 3 fatty acids and is a good source of fat for damp individuals. Avoid excess salt or electrolytes which will hold more dampness in the body. Probiotics are helpful because they support digestion, which can be weak in these horses.

- **Management:** Ideally these horses should be kept outside in the fresh air, but if they must be stalled use a fan to keep the air circulating. Provide as dry an environment as possible and remove all wet bedding from stalls daily. Sand may be the best bedding choice, as shavings and straw tend to hold moisture.

- **Topical Treatment:** Tea tree oil is very good for treating skin infections and irritations in damp horses. Body washes with diluted liniment or witch hazel will have a nice astringent and antiseptic effect without being overly drying.

Dry Skin Conditions

At the other end of the scale, some types of horses are especially affected by dryness. In these horses, skin conditions show up with extreme itchiness, dry skin, and hair loss, but with no obvious skin lesions. Although bathing or washing might seem indicated for dry, itchy skin, these activities will only further dry the skin on these horses by removing natural oils.

Treatment for Dry Skin Conditions

- ***Diet:*** Soybean based proteins, barley, and dairy-based products such as Calf Manna are excellent for horses with dry, itchy skin. Small amounts of salt or electrolytes added to their feed will help to moisten the tissues. Seaweeds such as kelp also have a moisturizing effect on the body. Soybean oil, rice bran, or flax seed oil can be added to the feed to improve coat quality, and a little bit of molasses is fine for these horses if it does not make them too hyper.

- ***Management:*** These horses are very itchy, so insect bites really aggravate them. Provide a covered area with excellent ventilation to keep insect exposure to a minimum. Do not bathe or shampoo these horses unless absolutely necessary, as that will just further dry out the skin, making them even more itchy.

- ***Topical Treatment:*** Avoid alcohol-based insect repellents, as alcohol is another drying agent. One part AVON Skin So Soft mixed with one part vinegar makes an excellent repellent which also lubricates the skin. If one must bathe the horse, oatmeal-based shampoos are a good choice because they are soothing and will help with itching.

Insect Related Skin Conditions

Insects can cause horses no small amount of irritation, especially in warm or damp climates. Here are some holistic ways to treat your horse when insect-related skin conditions crop up:

- ***Insect Bites:*** Fly bites appear as bumps with or without hair loss. They have a crust in the middle and may be painful or itchy. Horse and deer flies commonly bite the lower body, legs, neck, and withers. Stable flies bite the neck, back, chest, groin, and legs. Horses can develop hypersensitive reactions to fly bites. Stabling from before dawn until after sunset may limit exposure, as flies prefer fairly bright light. Good sanitation, fly traps, and fly predators (tiny, harmless insects that feed on fly larvae) will help keep fly populations down. Mosquito bites are similar to fly bites but have no crusts. Heavy attacks by mosquitoes may result in hives, which generally disappear in three to four days.

Mosquitoes are best controlled by eliminating breeding grounds such as swampy areas and containers that hold rain water.

Goldfish or minnows in horse troughs will eat mosquito larvae, and AVON Skin So Soft mixed 50/50 with water or apple cider vinegar will help repel adult mosquitoes.

- ***Hypersensitivity Reactions:*** Culicoides is a genus of biting gnats that cause hair loss and itching in horses sensitive to them (this condition is also called Queensland Itch or Sweet Itch). These gnats breed around the edges of ponds, springs, and creeks. They also breed in compost piles, manure, or any other wet vegetable matter. Adult gnats are most active when there is little or no breeze and temperatures are warm. They may be active year round in the south. Favored feeding sites on the horse include the ears, poll, mane, withers, tail, head, ventral abdomen, and flanks. Because these gnats only cause symptoms in hypersensitive horses, not all animals in the herd are affected. Horses may develop secondary lesions due to self-mutilation from severe itching. Often the mane and tail will be rubbed out, and sores may appear on the belly from constant rubbing on the ground, low limbs, or stumps. Some relief can be obtained by mixing 24 ounces of AVON Skin So Soft, one quart witch hazel, and one pound Epsom salts, then spraying or wiping down the horse several times a day. The best defense against these pests is to stable animals from before sundown until well after sunrise, as most gnat species feed during the night, and especially at dawn and dusk. A three-sided shed is adequate if it has good ventilation. A fan may be needed on still days. The conventional approach to countering an excessive immune response to these gnats is to give corticosteroids, but I have found that starting horses on blue-green algae before the gnat season will modify their reactions to the bites.

In summary, to help control insect-related dermatitis the best approach is management, including good sanitation, avoiding exposure, and good nutrition to keep the skin and immune system healthy. A handful of dried calendula flowers added daily to the feed may help with itchiness. Feeding apple cider vinegar at the rate of one-half to one cup a day may decrease fly bites. If you must use chemical fly repellents, apply them sparingly and focus on the legs of the horse and not the whole body. Avoid vaccinations in horses prone to hypersensitivity reactions and consider homeopathy, chiropractic, or acupuncture to help rebalance the immune system. Conventional treatment may be needed on a short-term basis to give relief to the horse and to allow deep acting treatments time to take effect.

Parasitic Skin Conditions
Habronemiasis (Summer Sores)

This condition is due to a hypersensitivity reaction to the equine stomach worm. The adult worms live in nodular lesions of the stomach wall and produce larvae that are passed in the manure. Flies pick up the larvae and deposit them around wounds and moist places on the body, such as the eye, sheath, and penis. These sores appear when the ambient temperature remains above 70 degrees and heal with the onset of cold weather. Certain horses seem to be more susceptible and have lesions year after year, while herd mates are not affected.

Lesions first appear as slowly healing wounds that enlarge and develop exuberant granulation tissue. Itching may be mild to severe. These sores assume a circular appearance as they enlarge. Calcified granules containing dead larvae are highly suggestive of habronemiasis. Local and systemic corticosteroids are effective but have associated side effects. Supporting the overall health of your horse is the best prevention for summer sores, and homeopathy can be effective in rebalancing the immune system. The only effective topical treatments that I have found for summer sores include corticosteroids such as Panalog or a homemade mixture of Furacin, DMSO, and Azium in equal parts.

Dermatophytosis (Ringworm)

Dermatophytosis is a superficial fungal infection of the skin, hair, and/or hooves caused mainly by the fungi Microsporum and Trichophyton. Warm, damp, dirty conditions encourage fungal infection, while sufficient sun and fresh air discourage it. Natural infection results from direct contact with infected animals or people, or from contaminated soil. Indirect infection can be acquired through contaminated equipment such as grooming tools, tack, and blankets. Biting insects may also spread infection.

Dietary inadequacies may predispose horses to this type of infection, and youngsters are particularly prone to ringworm. Also animals on prolonged antibiotics or immunosuppressive therapy are at greater risk. The incubation period is usually one to four weeks.

Minor trauma to the skin is necessary for fungus to gain access to the deeper epidermal cells. Once the fungus has penetrated the skin it releases toxins that cause inflammation and induce a hypersensitivity reaction. Hair loss results from infection of the hair shafts, which makes them brittle and susceptible to breakage. The lesions spread in a circular fashion. Death of infected hair and the immune response effectively stop fungal growth in the center of the lesion while the growth spreads outward.

Typical clinical features of a fungal infection include scaling, crusting, and hair loss. Lesions can occur anywhere on the body but appear most often in areas which contact equipment. When these fungal infections occur in the pastern area they are often referred to as "scratches" or "grease heel." About one-third of infected horses will be itchy, and a few horses manifest some pain.

Diagnosis is based on a culture of broken hair collected from the periphery of lesions. Fungal cultures take ten days to two weeks to produce results. In a horse with a competent immune system lesions will regress spontaneously, however this process can be aided by a natural antifungal product such as tea tree oil. There are several mild skin medications for horses that contain essential oils, herbs, and tea tree oil. These are much safer to use than iodine or chlorhexidine disinfectants. You can use the chemicals to clean your tack and grooming equipment, but applied to skin they will remove protective fatty acids from the skin and further break down the skin's natural defense system.

The best treatment and prevention of fungal infection comes from keeping your horse in a clean dry environment and feeding him a whole-food, nutritious diet. If infection occurs due to hot humid conditions, avoid bathing and instead give a sponge bath with diluted liniment. The liniment is a mild antiseptic that will also remove sweat (plus it contains oils that will help repel additional moisture). If infection occurs due to damp cold conditions, try extra brushing with a clean soft brush to keep the skin clean, stimulate circulation, and release natural oils.

If your horse is especially prone to fungus, consider ... treatment to strengthen his immune system as well as a more ... diet. I often suggest blue-green algae since it is high in beta car... which the body converts to vitamin A and which has been proven ... stimulate the immune system.

Cutaneous Onchocerciasis (Onchocerca)

Hypersensitivity to onchocerca can occur year round which helps distinguish it from some of the other more seasonal skin conditions. Onchocerca is a thread-like nematode that resides in the nuchal ligament (thick ligament under the mane) and produces microfilaria (baby worms) that migrate to the skin. Microfilaria are found in the largest numbers along the ventral midline, chest, withers, inguinal or groin region, and eyelids. The initial lesion of cutaneous onchocerciasis consists of thinning hair, with or without mild scaling or crusting, especially about the face, neck, chest, withers, and ventral midline. There may be mild to severe itching. Lesions at the center of the forehead are often considered to be a hallmark of cutaneous onchocerciasis. Tail rubbing is seldom seen, which helps differentiate this skin condition from hypersensitivity to culicoides gnats.

Horses with healthy immune systems appear less susceptible to this condition. If hair loss and itching are a problem, ivermectin administered at two- to four-month intervals will help control the microfilaria.

Conclusion

The health of the skin and hair is a strong indicator of the internal health of your horse. Frequent skin conditions of any type can indicate nutritional deficiencies, an immune system imbalance, or toxicity. It is never a good idea to suppress skin conditions with strong medications, as this may only mask a more severe problem. In the cases I treat I am willing to tolerate a degree of itching or hair loss while I focus on raising the overall health of the horse.

Uveitis

Uveitis is also sometimes referred to as *periodic ophthalmia* or *moon blindness*. This condition is a chronic inflammation of the internal structures of the eye. Symptoms include pain, swelling, cloudiness of the cornea, pus in the anterior chamber of the eye, and contraction of the pupil.

:quent flare-ups will often respond to steroids,
nmatory drugs, and atropine, but relapse
nonths after treatment is stopped. Each attack
) the eye, eventually leading to blindness. The
/ starts in one eye but moves to the other eye,
lness.

Several causative ractors have been suggested for anterior uveitis. Some horses with uveitis will have elevated titers to leptospira, an organism which primarily affects cattle. B-vitamin deficiency has also been considered. The bottom line is that this is an autoimmune disease, meaning the immune system is out of balance and is attacking the horse's own eye tissue.

After many frustrating years of treating this condition with Western medicine, I have moved away from drugs to focus more on rebalancing the immune system. When I am consulted about a horse with an acute flare-up, my first focus is to control the pain and inflammation. I have had good results with a solution of half hypericum tincture and half calendula tincture diluted at the ratio of ten drops tincture to one ounce of water or saline solution. A gauze sponge is soaked with this solution and placed as a poultice over the eye. I do not try to get the solution into the eye directly. Horses seem to experience excellent relief with this treatment and will often lower their heads and become very relaxed. This application can be repeated four to six times a day. I find frequent attempts to force medications into the eye can cause more inflammation and create great resistance in the horse. An exception would be if the horse has an actual ulcer of the cornea that might require antibiotic treatment. Rather than using systemic non-steroidal anti-inflammatory agents, I have had some good success with B-L solution, which is a mixture of devil's claw and yucca.

I also start these horses on a product from Standard Process called Oculotrophin. The theory behind this product is that the inflammation itself becomes a trigger for further immune system attacks, so it is made from eye tissue that has been treated to extract the antigen to which the immune system is reacting. The theory is that when you feed this type of substance it will be absorbed, and the immune system will be occupied with it rather than with attacking the eye itself. Once the horse's eye has had time to heal, it will not continue to attract the immune system as it did when it was in a state of constant inflammation. I find the Oculotrophin needs to be fed continuously for six to twelve months in some cases.

To address any nutrient deficiencies, I feed large amounts of a Cell Tech product called Sprouts & Algae. This product is very high in beta carotene and supplies the body with natural concentrated nutrients to make super-oxide dismutase—a potent anti-oxidant.

Once the acute flare-up has quieted down, I start with constitutional treatment to balance the immune system. I generally use homeopathy and take a full history to include other health issues that the horse has experienced. I suggest vaccinations be discontinued because they can trigger attacks by stimulating the immune system. I suggest blue-green algae be added to the diet because of its high chlorophyll content. I warn owners to expect further flare-ups, as this condition is very difficult to treat, but the attacks should gradually become less frequent and less severe.

Anhydrosis

Anhydrosis is the scientific term for the inability to sweat. This condition appears to be becoming more common in horses. Affected horses sweat normally during the cooler months, but lose that ability when the weather turns warm and humid. Racing and competition horses are the most commonly affected. These horses cannot cool themselves, so they must be worked very carefully, if at all, during warmer months.

There is no scientifically proven explanation for anhydrosis and no effective conventional treatment other than moving to a cooler climate. My theory, which I describe below, is that anhydrosis develops because the immune system is weak. This theory is based on Traditional Chinese Medicine (TCM).

At the basis of TCM is the concept of Qi. Qi can be translated as "energy," "life force," or "vital force." There are several types of Qi: Original Qi, Food Qi, Gathering Qi, True Qi, Nutritive Qi, and Defensive Qi. Nutritive Qi is in the Interior and nourishes. Defensive Qi is on the Exterior and protects. With anhydrosis the main concern is with the Defensive Qi or "Wei Qi." Wei Qi circulates under the skin and its main function is to protect the body from attacks of external pathogens. Remember, in TCM the concern is not with viruses and bacteria, but with external pathogenic factors, such as Wind, Cold, Heat, and Damp. Wei Qi also warms, moistens, and partially nourishes skin and muscles, and adjusts the opening and closing of the pores, which regulates sweating and body temperature.

Let's now look at how a horse could be set up for anhydrosis based on this theory. We take a horse and stress him with training and competition, and then we give him multiple vaccinations. This weakens the Defensive Wei Qi. Even on the "best" processed diets, nutritional deficiencies further stress his system. Another common practice is cooling down hot horses with cold-water hosing, which, while not a problem in a horse with strong Wei Qi, in a weakened horse could allow the pathogenic factor Cold to invade and contract the pores, inhibiting the proper function of the sweat glands within the pores. Weak Defensive Wei Qi can also allow pathogenic Heat to enter the body, causing excessive sweating initially, which then depletes the body fluids and eventually leads to the inability to sweat. Most horses with anhydrosis exhibit other signs of immune system weakness such as chronic cough, chronic lameness or stiffness, muscle pain, or allergies.

Treatment of Anhydrosis

To treat anhydrosis we must rebuild the immune system first and foremost. The diet should be improved by feeding whole grains rather than processed feeds. Extra Vitamin C and E may be indicated. Probiotics will help support good digestion and assimilation of nutrients. Electrolytes offered free choice, or fed to the horse that is sweating excessively, may help prevent anhydrosis. Blue-green algae has been proven to support immune function and would be a good addition to the diet. Homeopathic remedies can be used to help reverse the ill effects of vaccinations and rebalance the horse's system. Acupuncture can be used to rebuild the Defensive Wei Qi and repel external pathogenic factors. In summary, to prevent anhydrosis you should feed a good whole food diet (including electrolytes if indicated), minimize training stress, vaccinate as little as possible, and sponge off hot horses rather than hose them down with cold water.

Leaky Gut Syndrome

Conventional Western veterinarians are now recognizing and treating equine ulcers more frequently. With increased awareness of this syndrome, more horses are routinely being given antacids and acid-blocking drugs. These medications may temporarily give relief only to set the horse up for more serious chronic health problems.

The mucosal lining of the digestive tract is like an internal skin or barrier, similar to the skin outside the body. When the lining is healthy, it prevents bacteria, large protein molecules (antigens), and toxins from entering the blood. If it is not healthy, the blood becomes contaminated, and in turn the internal organs, especially the liver, become damaged.

How Damage Occurs

A healthy mucosal lining has a protective barrier made of the mucous layer as well as large numbers of beneficial bacteria, which prevents toxins from having direct contact with the epithelial surface. Non-steroidal anti-inflammatory drugs interfere with secretion of mucous, and antibiotics decrease healthy gut flora (bacteria), so these drugs alone or in combination can set the stage for leaky gut syndrome. Antacids and acid-blocking drugs also upset the normal pH (acid/alkaline balance) in the intestinal tract, creating a hostile environment for healthy bacteria and an attractive environment for pathogenic bacteria.

Bacterial dysbiosis is an imbalance between normal and pathogenic gut flora. This condition creates a very unhealthy gastrointestinal system that then impairs proper digestion and absorption of nutrients and irritates the intestinal lining. Other causes of leaky gut syndrome include surgery, injury, chronic intestinal infection, drugs such as antibiotics and anti-inflammatories, malnutrition, and vaccinations.

Pathology Associated with Leaky Gut Syndrome

To prevent noxious substances from entering the bloodstream, the healthy gut responds in a complex, highly integrated fashion. Enterocytes, or gut-lining cells, actually bind the noxious substance and release chemicals to destroy it. These cells then secrete substances which draw fluids into the interior of the gut and wash away the offending substance. Damage to the mucous lining and enterocytes often takes the form of weak places in the gut wall, which then allows large protein molecules and other antigens to invade the bloodstream. When these antigens, which may even include poorly digested food particles, pass through the intestinal wall, the immune system reacts by forming antibodies to combat them. This is the foundation for many food allergies and auto-immune conditions. Antigen/antibody complexes can also create allergic reactions such as urticaria (hives), skin eruptions, or chronic obstructive pulmonary disease (heaves).

Stiffness and joint soreness can also be related to leaky gut syndrome. This results when antigen/antibody complexes are deposited in the tissues. Toxins released into the bloodstream can also cause fever of unknown origin and general fatigue. Other symptoms include memory loss, mood swings, shortness of breath, poor exercise tolerance, or hyperactivity. Intestinal symptoms include irritable bowel syndrome, inflammatory bowel disease, or bacterial infections in the bowel.

Most of these conditions manifest in the horse as colic, which is often recurrent and unrelated to management. Chronic weight loss and chronic diarrhea may also result from leaky gut syndrome.

Leaky gut syndrome has a devastating effect on the liver because it is the organ that is called upon to clean up all this contaminated blood coming from the intestine. When the liver is stressed, symptoms of liver dysfunction begin to appear. These include tight sore muscles; poor quality hooves; weak, easily injured tendons and ligaments; eye disorders; and irritability. These symptoms precede any elevation in liver enzymes that would show up on routine bloodwork. The increased release of toxins into the blood will also deplete the body's store of detoxification enzymes, leading to an excess of circulating free radicals. These free radicals contribute to chronic diseases such as laminitis.

Laminitis

Laminitis, or inflammation of the equine hoof, is an extremely serious condition and in its chronic form involves multiple symptoms of metabolic imbalance. Bringing a laminitic horse back to health can take a long time and is very emotionally draining. Treatment options are highly controversial, from dietary concerns to farrier issues. Doing justice to this illness here would require an entire second book, so this section is intended only to familiarize those of you who are dealing with this issue with some basic guidelines regarding the disease, and, hopefully, to help you formulate a plan of action that will best suit you and your horse. For a much more in-depth look at how to deal with a laminitic horse in as natural a way possible, please see the Resources Appendix for directions on how to order my Ebook on this topic. It is important for you to know that there is hope in these cases, so it is well worth your time to research this topic thoroughly!

With the acute form of laminitis (previously covered under First Aid), prompt aggressive treatment aimed at relieving the inflammation and removing the predisposing cause will usually prevent any permanent damage to the foot. The chronic laminitis case, unfortunately, presents more of a challenge. Most chronic laminitis cases involve some degree of coffin bone rotation, multiple symptoms of metabolic imbalance such as Cushing's disease or insulin resistance, and no obvious predisposing causes. These horses are systemically ill and require diligent ongoing care to fully recover.

I prefer to treat these horses without shoes. A properly done barefoot trim will help restore normal hoof function and increase circulation to the foot. Trims must be done on a weekly basis and the horse must exercise to bring circulation back into the foot. Jaime Jackson and Pete Ramey have excellent books on barefoot trimming. Your farrier will need to study these principles before attempting to manage a laminitic horse.

If shoes are used I prefer natural balance shoes which move the breakover back from the front of the toe and offer good support for the heel. Pads may also be needed to distribute the weight over the frog and sole and relieve pressure off the damaged wall tissue. Shoeing or trimming must be done by a competent farrier who has worked before with foundered horses. These horses have special needs and the shoeing interval must be regular and tailored to those needs. Amazingly, owners will spend thousands of dollars to save a foundered horse but then neglect hoof care after the crisis is past.

Diet for Laminitic Horses
Laminitis calls for a simple diet low in carbohydrates and high in fiber. Purina Equine Senior is a good feed for some foundered horses and others do well on a small amount of oats or barley. Probiotics support the digestive function and limit the production of endotoxins (toxins produced by pathogenic bacteria). Blue-green algae provides a source of food-based vitamins, minerals, and antioxidants. Small doses of antioxidants such as coenzyme Q10 (CoQ10) may be indicated. You should not need to give more than 60-120 mg a day of a good quality CoQ10 product like those produced by Cell Tech, Nutramax, or Thorne brands. Generic brands of CoQ10 may not be active.

Turnout on lush grass should be approached cautiously. Many laminitis horses have hormone imbalances that affect their sugar metabolism, and fast-growing, lush grass is high in sugar. As your horse gets healthier he should become better able to tolerate fresh grass. I suggest gradually increasing exposure to grass over several weeks and monitoring digital pulses. It is also best to avoid hay that has been heavily fertilized.

Prevention

- Stop vaccinations.

- Take horses off high carbohydrate rations.

- Allow horses more exercise.

- Use a minimum of drugs and chemicals, including insecticides.

- Do not allow access to highly fertilized hays or pasture.

- Provide fresh, clean, non-chlorinated water.

- Provide a good quality, broad-spectrum vitamin and mineral supplement that is easily absorbed and assimilated by the body.

- Provide regular hoof care.

- Try not to overstress the horse.

- Always be on the lookout for early signs of laminitis. It is a disease which is easier to prevent than treat. Once symptoms appear, one should approach the case as a systemic illness that will require long-term care.

The Road Back to Health

In closing, I want to say that cure is always my desired outcome with chronic laminitis cases. This means a complete return to full function without need for continued treatments or expensive management practices. Sometimes it is simply not possible, especially with advanced pathology such as pituitary tumors or severe bone damage, and with these cases, palliation with remedies, special hoof care, and high levels of antioxidant nutritional or herbal supplements may be needed. Most cases, however, can be cured with good homeopathic prescribing and proper management. The challenge is staying alert to shifting symptom patterns and resisting the temptation to palliate with large doses of herbs or supplements. Chronic laminitis cases are perhaps the most difficult to work with, and yet they can also be the most rewarding.

Chapter 11
Competition Related Disorders

Inflammatory Airway Disease (IAD)

When most horse owners think of lower respiratory disease they think of serious conditions such as pneumonia or heaves. Performance horse owners, on the other hand, realize that low-grade inflammation in the lower respiratory tract can cause trouble long before obvious clinical signs are apparent. A mild cough with a slight mucous discharge might mean only mild irritation, which would respond to a few days of rest— or it might be a sign of more serious trouble.

Most but not all horses with IAD have a persistent cough that lasts longer than four weeks. Coughing is not normal if it shows up consistently at the beginning of exercise, occurs spontaneously in the barn or during feeding, is deep or productive, or reduces performance in any way. Other signs of IAD that may show up less consistently include fading at the end of a race, moving the jaws or swallowing after a cough, and reluctance to collect or flex at the poll. IAD should also be considered when horses show increasing reluctance to work for no obvious reasons.

Unlike heaves, the specific cause of IAD is not known. It is most likely the result of multiple insults. Performance horses are subjected to many irritants that are present in barns, trailers, and dusty warm-up pens, in addition to facing the constant challenge of viruses and bacteria. It can be difficult to determine whether a horse has IAD or a primary infection caused by a virus or bacteria, since the symptom patterns can be very similar. Whereas viruses are rarely identified in transtracheal wash samples, bacteria commonly are; but again, in either case—viral or bacterial—we have no way of knowing whether those pathogens might have caused the inflammation or are present because of the inflammation. Antibiotics are often prescribed based on the culture and sensitivity results for the bacteria found in the transtracheal wash sample, but it is then not uncommon for subsequent samples to reveal the presence of an entirely new bacterial infection. From a holistic viewpoint, this would suggest that bacteria are present because of the inflammation rather than the other way around, in which case the focus should be on decreasing the inflammation instead of treating an infection.

Diagnosis of IAD is based on a combination of clinical signs, the results of an endoscopic exam, transtracheal and bronchoalveolar wash results, and the horse's response to treatment. If you suspect that your horse has IAD, you can support his respiratory tract and immune system by taking a few extra precautions such as the following.

- **Probiotics:** Probiotics, especially acidophilus, produce substances which are antiviral and antifungal. Probiotics also support the immune system by supporting the function of the digestive system.

- **Decongestant Herbs:** In general, herbs can be very helpful in supporting the respiratory tract. Decongestant herbs like ephedra help clear excess mucous by dilating the small airways. Be aware that this herb may test positive so it should not be used during competition. This herb should not be used without the guidance of an experienced herbalist.

- **Demulcent/Expectorant Herbs:** Marshmallow, slippery elm, comfrey, mullein, and fenugreek help thin and clear out mucous.

- **Antispasmodic Herbs:** Lobelia is an antispasmodic that can relax spasms in the small airways. This is a very strong herb and should not be used without the guidance of an experienced herbalist.

- **Beta Glucan:** Pure, whole particle beta glucan helps with inflammation by mobilizing white blood cells to areas of injury or inflammation. These white blood cells (macrophages) then remove damaged tissue quickly before it has time to trigger more inflammation.

- **Vitamin C and Bioflavanoids:** These two supplements provide potent antioxidant benefits and support healing of the lung tissue. Citrus C/Q from Equilite is an especially good product that contains these antioxidants.

- **Noni Juice:** Noni is a natural anti-inflammatory which is high in naturally occurring antioxidants.

- **Nosodes:** Occasionally a certain farm will have a high incidence of IAD, which can be due to many factors including environmental irritants or resident viral, bacterial, or fungal pathogens. If this situation develops and healthy horses introduced to the farm develop symptoms, it may be valuable to make a homeopathic nosode to be given to all horses on the farm and all new horses as they are brought in. To do this, samples from a transtracheal wash are sent on ice immediately to a homeopathic pharmacy where a remedy is made based on homeopathic principles. This principle is similar to vaccination but no harmful substances are included, and the action is specific to the pathogen on a particular farm.

Antihistamines are rarely effective in treating IAD and, while antibiotics and bronchodialators may give temporary relief, they do not address the underlying inflammation. Corticosteroids are the Western treatment of choice but they are palliative at best and suppress the immune system, making the horse even more susceptible to infection. Side effects of steroids also include gastrointestinal bleeding and organ damage.

You can take active steps to prevent IAD from occurring:

- **Bedding:** Keep all bedding in the horse's stall and trailer clean and fresh in order to avoid mold and ammonia fumes. Fine particles of manure can also be very irritating when inhaled.

- **Nutritional Support:** Cell Tech's Animal Matrix for Horses is an excellent source of nutritional support because it contains probiotics, wheat sprouts, and blue-green algae. This combination is an excellent source of vitamins and minerals, and provides antioxidant support.

- **Noni Juice:** Used on a regular basis, noni can stop any respiratory inflammation before it becomes problematic.

- **Dust Control:** Keep your arena well watered and exercise your horse away from dusty warm-up areas whenever possible.

- **Bodywork:** Horses must be able to breathe deeply to clear their lungs. If you horse is very muscle sore or has a fixated rib he may be breathing shallowly. In the absence of deep breathing, your horse may be unable to clear mucous and inhaled debris from the deeper airways, setting up the potential for bronchial infection and inflammation. Regular bodywork will allow you to detect these problems so that free breathing can be restored quickly.

Exercise Induced Pulmonary Hemorrhage (EIPH)

A certain amount of pulmonary hemorrhage (called EIPH), which is bleeding in the lungs, can occur in any horse engaged in fast or intense exercise. The amount of bleeding can range from just a few red blood cells, detectable only by sensitive tests such as a bronchoalveolar lavage (BAL), to the much more obvious nosebleed. The greater the severity of EIPH, the more the horse's health is affected. Blood in the lungs acts as an irritant resulting in inflammation, and also creates an ideal breeding ground for bacteria.

The most widely accepted theory about the cause of EIPH is that the high blood pressure from heavy exercise coupled with vacuum-like effects that occur during a deep inhalation causes the capillaries to rupture. The only gap in this theory is that it does not explain why almost all of the bleeding occurs in the upper back lobes of the lungs rather than uniformly throughout.

Another theory that helps to explain the location of the bleeding focuses on the anatomy of the running horse. Since a horse's forelegs are not attached to the spine with any bony structures, the action of running causes the shoulders to compress the ribcage. This wave of pressure then spreads outwards causing a shearing force on the tissue in the upper back of the lungs, resulting in bleeding. This type of hemorrhage is similar to the bleeding that occurs from a blunt trauma to the front of the chest or head—that is, the bleeding does not occur at the location of the trauma but on the opposite side of the body. This theory might explain why some horses are more likely to bleed after running on a hard surface, and why some "bleeders" do not respond to Lasix (furosemide).

I have my own additional theory as to why horses bleed. I feel that EIPH occurs because of weakened capillaries secondary to inadequate nutrition. Just as some people bruise easily, some horses bleed easily. The bleeding in horses, however, does not go into the tissues but moves instead into the airways. Many horses also have thick, toxic, and poorly oxygenated blood due to repeated exposure to chemicals and drugs, causing the heart to work harder and the blood pressure to rise. This increased arterial blood pressure, with or without weakened capillary walls, sets the stage for EIPH.

To definitively diagnose and determine the severity of EIPH it is best to do an endoscopic exam 30 minutes to one hour following intense exercise. A sample scoring system for diagnosing EIPH might include the following grades:

- Grade 1: Flecks of blood in the trachea
- Grade 2: More blood than Grade 1, but less than a continuous stream
- Grade 3: A continuous stream smaller than half the tracheal width
- Grade 4: A continuous stream greater than half the tracheal width
- Grade 5: Airways awash with blood

Treatment and Prevention of EIPH

For many horses, 250 to 500 milligrams of Lasix (a potent diuretic) given one to four hours before a race will reduce blood pressure and prevent bleeding. For a significant number of other horses, however, Lasix is ineffective. In these cases it may be worth looking into the concussion theory as a cause of bleeding. While hard ground is certainly a factor in these cases, I suspect that many of these horses also run with a greater percentage of their weight on the forehand rather than working off the hindquarters.

Another factor to consider is upper airway resistance caused by the combination of blood pressure and inhalation vacuum pressure. Conditions such as laryngeal hemiplegia (a whistling or roaring that can be heard when the horse is breathing deeply from exertion), dorsal displacement of the soft palate, nasal, pharyngeal (at the back of the throat) or tracheal collapse, guttural pouch disease, excessive head flexion, or pharyngeal inflammation could cause an increase of the pressure in the lungs during inhalation. Treating any of these conditions would remove the underlying cause and may remedy the bleeding.

Herbal supplements can be useful in preventing EIPH. Many herbal supplements contain vitamin C and bioflavonoids, both of which support capillary integrity. Also useful are supplements that have mullein, yarrow, and lungwort, which reduce inflammation and strengthen weakened tissue, and shepherd's purse, which has coagulant factors. While I do not believe that a primary deficiency of clotting factors is the cause of EIPH, these clotting factors can be depleted by frequent bleeding episodes.

You can keep your horse's blood clean and well oxygenated with careful management that includes:

- Feeding whole food nutrition that includes supplements such as probiotics, antioxidants, and blue-green algae
- Avoiding drugs, excessive vaccination, and chemicals

Lasix is the most effective preventative for EIPH for horses that respond to it, but it is still important to explore all the possible factors that might cause your horse to bleed. Make every effort to keep your horse as healthy as possible, but do not risk a severe episode of bleeding by withholding Lasix if you know it to be effective for your horse. In order to receive the full benefit of the diuretic action of Lasix, water must be withheld between giving the dose and the time of intense exertion. Therefore, as soon as possible afterward, replenish your horse's electrolytes and offer plenty of fresh, free-choice water to combat dehydration. Some research suggests that smaller doses given closer to the actual run (250 mg. one hour before a race) can be effective.

Gastric Ulcers and Behavior Problems

When your normally well-behaved performance horse starts acting strangely, what do you do? Do you immediately think he's developing an attitude or do you look for other causes? If your horse demonstrates any or all of the behaviors below you may want to think twice before assuming he has an attitude problem:

- Refusing jumps
- Acting up in the alley way
- Kicking in the trailer
- Pinning his ears when you put your leg on
- Biting or kicking when his girth is tightened

While these may seem like a group of unrelated symptoms, they're not. They are common symptoms in horses with ulcers. Veterinarians and other researchers have recently recognized gastric and colonic ulcers as serious health threats, especially among performance horses or horses in training. The reasons ulcers are so common among these horses include:

- Infrequent high carbohydrate meals plus inadequate access to hay or pasture

- Heavy training schedules
- High stress environments
- Excessive use of drugs, especially non-steroidal anti-inflammatory drugs

Since most of the research has focused on gastric ulcers (rather than colonic), we know quite a bit about the factors that cause them. One of the major causes is inadequate access to free choice hay or pasture. Horses are meant to eat continuously, so their stomachs secrete acid constantly. When they are able to graze constantly they secrete saliva, which has a buffering effect on the stomach acid.

Plus, the hay or grass forms a fibrous mat-like barrier between the acid in the lower portion of the stomach (where digestion is occurring) and the upper portion of the stomach, which cannot tolerate contact with the acid. The lower part of the stomach is protected by mucous while the upper part is not, so ulcers tend to form when acid moves into the upper portion of the stomach.

A heavy exercise or training schedule can be another factor that can lead to gastric ulcers. When a horse exercises, he contracts his abdominal muscles, disrupting the protective fibrous mat in his stomach and forcing acid into its upper portion. Performance horses living in stalls may tense their abdominal muscles even when they are not exercising, since regular barn activities may prevent them from fully relaxing, especially if they are not offered free choice hay to occupy their time. In contrast, horses living in pasture move about slowly in a relaxed manner.

A third cause of ulcers in performance horses is trailering. Horses must frequently tense their abdominal muscles to maintain balance in a moving trailer, which tends to have the same effect as heavy exercise. Since many people do not offer hay when hauling, their horses are faced with long, uncomfortable rides. It's no wonder that many horses start kicking and pawing in the trailer!

Finally, tightening the girth when saddling is another source of discomfort for a horse with ulcers. It can cause contraction of the stomach muscles, forcing the acid into contact with any existing ulcers and aggravating ulcer pain.

When a horse must be kept in training, treating ulcers can be challenging. Most pharmaceutical products designed to treat ulcers act by blocking acid secretion. While this may be effective on a short-term basis, it eventually interferes with proper digestion and adversely affects the health of the digestive system. Keeping your horse in as natural an environment as possible is best, including offering free choice hay, building digestive health, and providing nutritional support so the body can rapidly heal the ulcerated tissue.

For nutritional support, I like to feed Purina Equine Senior rather than grain and add regular Cell Tech Essentials, which provide probiotics, digestive enzymes, and blue-green algae to support and heal the digestive system. I have also had success with a new product called SUCCEED, which is designed to support, protect and heal the digestive tract without interfering with normal acid production. I have done field testing with this product and have been very impressed with its effect on the behavior of horses with ulcers who had not responded completely to other measures. Whenever possible, keep hay in front of your horse so he has something to nibble on continuously.

Noni juice is another good food-based nutritional supplement to help your performance horse handle the rigors of training and competition. The natural anti-inflammatory properties of noni juice allow the horse to recover faster and have less muscle soreness.

Horses cannot use words to communicate with us so they have to send us signals when things are not right. How many times do we confuse their attempts to communicate with a bad attitude? When a horse is punished for trying to communicate it causes him even more stress and discomfort, and the downward spiral continues. How many good horses have had their careers cut short because of discomfort from ulcers? Try supporting your horse's digestive tract and see how his performance and attitude improve.

SECTION FOUR: PERFORMANCE HORSES

Chapter 12
Training the Performance Horse

After 26 years of veterinary practice I've seen a lot of performance horses break down and become unable to perform. What surprises me is that poor conformation and old age are rarely responsible for such breakdowns. In fact, my experience shows me that most breakdowns can be prevented, and that horses who are well cared for should be able to perform at very high levels well into their teens, if not into their early twenties. Some of the major causes contributing to early breakdown include:

- The horse's unsuitability (either mentally or physically) for the chosen discipline.

- Nutritional and digestive needs not being met given the additional stress placed upon performance horses.

- Lack of attention to stress management (high-performance horses are constantly under stress but great management and customized programs can easily lower stress levels).

- Improper training, which includes training too hard, inconsistent work, or doing the wrong types of drills for a particular body type and discipline.

This special Performance Horses section addresses these causes of early breakdown, and I hope contribute to the healthy longevity of our equine athlete companions.

Groundwork
Although most people think of horse training as being composed mostly of mounted exercises, I've found groundwork to be an essential part of the healthy and happy horse experience. Groundwork helps you build a solid foundation of trust and understanding with your horse, and ensures that both you and your horse will have fun and be safe. I've separated the groundwork exercises I recommend into two sections:

- Basic Groundwork: A review of the basics such as leading and backing.

- Groundwork for Gentling: Exercises for teaching your horse to respond appropriately in upsetting situations.

Since the more advanced exercises in the Gentling section build on the simpler ones in the Basic section, it is best to master the exercises in the Basic Groundwork section first.

Basic Groundwork

The beauty of groundwork is that you can use it to fine-tune the relationship between you and your horse at any time, especially if the weather is foul or you don't have time for a full riding session. These basic groundwork exercises set the stage for work under saddle and allow you to introduce new concepts to your horse in a safe environment. Be sure to do all of them from both sides. As you do these exercises, it is important to introduce variety into your work and avoid dwelling on exercises your horse has mastered. It is equally important to break difficult exercises into smaller steps that your horse can more easily handle.

You can spend an entire session just on groundwork or eventually incorporate these exercises into your daily routine with your horse. Many top trainers do groundwork as they lead a horse in from the pasture, as they tack up, or as they walk from the barn to the arena. After a while, groundwork can become second nature to you and your horse—like a graceful language that you both speak without words— and the benefits are immense and amazing. Before you decide that groundwork is either tedious or boring, give it a try. You'll be quickly surprised by the positive results. The exercises covered in this Basic Groundwork section include:

- Leading
- Longeing
- Rolling the Hind
- Bringing the Front End Around
- Backing
- Backing in Circles
- Transitions

My thanks to Buck Brannaman—many of these exercises are adapted from and based on those described in his *Groundwork* book. Please refer to his book for excellent pictures of many of these exercises.

Leading Willingly Without Pressure on the Lead Rope

If you find yourself having to drag on the rope to get your horse to move, step back until you are behind his shoulder and drive him forward with the end of the lead rope. Then ask him to follow you once he is moving. Even well trained horses can get lazy. If a horse is dull on the lead rope he's likely to be dull under saddle. Proper leading keeps your horse light and responsive.

Longeing in a Circle Around You

Teaching your horse to walk, trot, and canter a 20-meter (60-foot) circle is time well spent. You may not always have access to a round pen, and longeing is an excellent way to help your horse get focused and work off a little extra energy before being ridden. Never allow your horse to plunge wildly around on the end of the longe line, but a few gentle crow hops can help your horse work out any kinks in his system. During longeing ensure that your horse keeps his attention on you and his nose tipped toward you, and that he maintains the correct bend on the circle.

Rolling the Hind End (Turn on the Forehand)

Once your horse is moving forward freely on the longe line or lead rope, you can tighten the circle and ask your horse to disengage his hindquarters by stepping across and under his body with the inside hind leg. This movement is like stepping on the clutch in a standard transmission vehicle. It prepares the horse for a new speed or direction. This maneuver is particularly valuable in disciplines where speed and turning are required.

Bringing the Front End Around (Turn on the Haunches)

After your horse has rolled his hind end by stepping up under his body with his inside hind leg, he should be positioned to bring his front end around to complete the change of direction. As your horse's head crosses the line in front of your body, extend your leading hand in the new direction and step up to what was the horse's outside shoulder. This drives rather than pulls the horse in the new direction. It takes practice to develop the correct timing for these moves and, in the beginning, it is fine for the horse to bend his body as he moves into the new direction. As his skills improve he will be able to execute a turn on the forehand or turn on the haunches with straightness or bend (depending on which is being asked for) through the neck and ribcage.

Backing With a Soft Feel or Collection

To back your horse, face the opposite direction of your horse and grasp the lead rope where it connects to the halter with your thumb turned down. Apply steady gentle backward pressure on the rope until your horse drops his nose toward his chest. Immediately release the pressure on the rope when your horse makes the slightest effort in that direction. If your horse raises or lowers his head while you have pressure on the rope, acknowledge his efforts to search for the place of softness but don't lighten your pressure on the rope until he tips his nose toward his chest. If your horse backs without softening, stop him and begin the exercise again. Once your horse gives his nose consistently, hold your contact on the rope until he thinks about shifting his weight back. Doing this exercise on the ground improves your timing so that you release your pressure the instant your horse makes the correct action. Your horse will respond to your timing with a great attitude—good timing means your horse will never be confused and is always rewarded for his efforts.

Backing in Circles

Once your horse is backing freely in a straight line and moving his diagonal pairs of legs in rhythm, you can introduce the more complex exercise of backing in circles. Begin by backing in a straight line. As your horse's outside front leg leaves the ground, move the hand holding the lead rope to the outside to direct the front leg to step out as well as back. Don't be surprised if your horse loses all rhythm at this point and gets stuck. He will have to make the appropriate adjustments in the movement of his hind legs to accommodate this change in direction. If both of you get stuck, try developing a deeper understanding of this exercise by getting down on your hands and knees and mimicking what you're asking your horse to do. This will give you a better idea of the physical coordination required to complete this exercise.

Transitions

Now that your horse is leading and backing with softness and lightness, ask him to do some simple transitions in hand. Start by walking beside him with your body even with his head. Break into a jog and ask your horse to keep pace with you. If he fails to do so, drop back behind his shoulder and drive him forward into a jog, then return to your position by his head. Slow to a walk again and ask your horse to stay with you. As your horse catches on to the rules of this "game," increase the difficulty by going from a trot to a halt, or from a trot to a soft back, and then return to a trot again. Keep your horse fresh by introducing new variations. Be sure and lead your horse from both sides, and when changing direction it is good to get in the habit of turning your horse away from you by driving his shoulder rather than pulling him toward you with the lead rope. This helps your horse stay more balanced and keeps him from leaning into you.

Groundwork Exercises for Gentling

The leading exercises we discussed in the Basic Groundwork section teach your horse to become light and responsive to your aids. In this section we focus on gentling exercises, which encourage your horse to be safe and dependable in any situation, especially scary ones! These exercises can literally be lifesavers for both you and your horse because they train your horse to respond rather than react with panic in new situations. They also teach your horse to look to and depend on you for cues as to how to respond under pressure. The exercises covered in this Groundwork Exercises for Gentling section include:

- Flag Work
- Sacking Out
- Rope Work
- Yielding to a Rope on the Leg

Flag Work

This exercise teaches your horse to remain calm around fluttering objects like jackets, tarps, and even butterflies! I wish I had known about this exercise before I rode my mule mare, Tess, for the first time with a wind breaker—when we came around a corner the wind caught my jacket and we were off! As you can imagine, the faster Tess ran the more my jacket flapped. To get her back under control I finally had to take the wind breaker off (with Tess still at a dead run) and toss it away. Now that I know about flagwork I look forward to never having another experience like that again!

You can easily make your own flag by attaching a plastic bag to the end of a dressage whip. Before you begin flagging make sure you and your horse are in a safe and enclosed area, like a round pen. Begin by standing a good distance away from your horse (four to six feet) while holding his lead rope and moving the flag gently up and down. This may startle him so don't be surprised if he moves away from you. If you've already practiced the groundwork exercises outlined in the previous section, you'll easily be able to roll his hind end if he moves away from you too quickly. Keep moving the flag up and down and rolling your horse's hind end until he stops moving away from you, then stop moving the flag, walk up to him, and pet him. If you find that your horse does not stop moving away from the flag within a short period of time, slow your movements with the flag and stop at the first sign that your horse is slowing down and trying to stop.

Continue with this exercise until your horse is totally unconcerned with the flag. If you stop before this point (i.e., when he tolerates the flag but is still concerned about it) your horse won't get as much benefit out of this lesson, and you may have to repeat it several times in the future. Once your horse is totally relaxed around the flag, start moving it closer and closer to his body. Continue until you can flutter the flag all around and over his body including his face and legs (be careful to avoid his eyes).

Sacking Out

You can do this exercise with a folded feed sack, lariat, or slicker. Start by folding your feed sack into a small square and rubbing your horse's neck with it. Allow him to move away if he gets anxious but try to keep the sack in contact with his neck. Continue until he stops or slows down, then remove the sack from his neck and pet him. Once your horse stays calm and

My mule Tess after being sacked out.

relaxed with the feed sack at his neck, move the sack to different parts of his body. If he moves away from you, keep him in a tight circle around you and, when he stops, remove the sack from the area of concern. This teaches your horse to move his feet in a controlled manner rather than simply bolting away from you when he is afraid. Once your horse is totally comfortable with the sack being rubbed all over his body, open the sack to its full expanse and slap it gently all over his body. You can repeat this exercise with any similar item that concerns your horse.

Rope Work

Even if you never intend to rope off your horse, it's still a good idea to do some rope work on and around his body. Rope work ensures that your horse won't panic if he gets caught in a fence or if the saddle slides back causing the back cinch to slap him in the belly. Begin by making a loop with your lariat and swinging it gently while standing next to your horse. Toss the loop near your horse, and then pull it back in. Be careful when you draw the rope into the blind spot directly below his nose because he may paw at the rope. When your horse is comfortable with you swinging the rope near him, toss it up on his back and let it drop over his hindquarters. Again, if he moves off let him go in a circle around you but try to keep the rope on him until he stops. When he stays relaxed with the rope draped on his hind end, allow him to step through the loop so that the rope runs between his hind legs. Repeat this maneuver on his front legs.

Yielding to a Rope on the Leg

This exercise is specifically aimed at teaching your horse to stay calm and relaxed if he gets caught in wire. You will need an assistant for the second half of this exercise. Start by placing the loop of your lariat around the pastern of one of his front legs. Hold the lead rope with one hand while using your other hand to apply pressure to the lariat. When your horse allows you to move his foot forward with the lariat, release the pressure and pet him. Repeat this process and move his foot a little further forward each time. Eventually you should be able to lead your horse by his front foot. Repeat this exercise on the other front foot.

Next you want to teach your horse to yield his back feet in response to pressure on the rope. For this exercise it's a good idea to wear leather gloves and chaps to prevent rope burns and bruises. Have your assistant take a loop of the lead rope around a stout fence post and stand on the opposite side of the fence or use a long rope so he can stay out of harm's way. Now place the loop of your lariat around one of your horse's back pasterns. Stand about 15 feet away from your horse, at about a 30-degree angle behind him, and gently apply pressure by pulling on the rope. Ask him to pick his foot up off the ground in response to the pressure from the rope. His first reaction will probably be to kick violently to free his foot. This is exactly the action that causes such severe injury when a horse gets caught in wire. Don't try to stop your horse from kicking but keep enough tension on the rope that your horse can't kick the loop off. Release the rope as soon as your horse stops kicking. Again ask your horse to yield his foot and relax the rope at the slightest response, such as resting the foot on the toe and letting you drag it backward. Your goal is to have your horse lift each back foot in response to the rope pressure and to hold his foot up with no resistance. This may take several sessions so be patient. In addition to preventing injury, this exercise also helps your horse learn how to balance on three legs.

Training for a Balanced Horse

Groundwork exercises are excellent for balancing your horse's mind, but what can you do to help your horse develop a more balanced body? To develop a physical training program for balance, I highly recommend that you evaluate your horse to see what kind of body type he has and then develop a program that will maintain his strengths while shoring up his physical weaknesses. This is often a balance between exercises that focus on collection versus extension.

I see so many top performance horses break down before their time because of an imbalanced training program that stresses one group of muscles over another. Based on my experience, I believe that training for equal development in both collection and extension muscles can prevent these early breakdowns and lead to healthier, happier show careers for many horses.

Muscle Types

Before discussing the different body types, I want to pause here to explain the simple difference between collection and extension muscles. Horses use their collection muscles to hold themselves upright and maintain good posture. They use their extension muscles for moving their bodies forward and for speed. Ideally, you want your horse to have good tone in his collection muscles, and mass and strength in his extension muscles. Dressage horses tend to use their collection muscles more while race horses and jumpers tend to use their extension muscles more.

What Body Type Does Your Horse Have?

Now that you know the difference between collection and extension muscles, the next step is to determine what body type your horse has: collection, extension, or balanced.

Collection

These horses have well-developed top lines with powerful backs and necks. They are usually short bodied, short backed, and have upright postures. Their body style makes it very easy for them to collect and bring their hindquarters underneath them. These horses also usually have short and broad heads and shorter legs. Collection horses excel at activities such as dressage, and the perfect example of a collection horse is a Lipizzaner.

"Jackson," QH/Percheron Cross—photo courtesy of Phil Giglio.

Extension

These horses tend to have long frames with powerfully developed chest, shoulder, lower neck, and hindquarter muscles. Their bodies are built for extension and speed rather than collection. They usually have longer backs, legs, and faces, and the perfect example of an extension horse is a Thoroughbred.

"Sail On Battle," an Appendix QH—photo courtesy of Joan Carlson.

Balanced

These horses have the ideal body type, with well-developed top lines and strong chest, shoulder, and hindquarter muscles. They are able to extend and collect with equal ease. The Morgan is an example of a horse whose extension and collection muscles are often quite well-balanced.

"Kate," QH—photo courtesy of Rita Digneo.

Having discussed horses that are strong in the collection muscles, strong in the extension muscles, and equally balanced between the two, let me also add that some horses are weak in both collection and extension muscles. Sometimes horses that are caught in this awkward position lack good conformation, but sometimes it is simply due to poor training. In either case, a well-balanced training program will help any horse improve.

A Balanced Training Program

To develop a balanced training program built around longevity and health, you want to assess both your horse's body type and your riding discipline. Usually, these two factors go hand in hand. For instance, if you compete in barrel racing, chances are that you are riding an extension horse built for speed. If, on the other hand, your focus is dressage, you've probably chosen a collection horse who can bring his back end underneath him with relative ease. Taking into consideration both your riding discipline and your horse's body type, see if you can balance your current training program with some of these suggested exercises:

- ### Collection Disciplines and Horses

  Collection horses, like those typically found in dressage, are asked to carry themselves in collection much of the time, which develops the collection muscles at the expense of the extension muscles. This can lead to a lack of speed and poor flexibility (because they rarely stretch their muscles). To correct this imbalance, work your horse's extension muscles by training for speed and strength. Alternate hill work and short bursts of speed with lateral work and long, low gaits. Encourage your horse to extend his stride with long walking and trotting, as well as extended cantering and short hand gallops.

- ### Extension Disciplines and Horses

  Racehorses, barrel racers, and jumpers rely on their extension muscles for speed but can break down early if they don't have well-developed collection muscles (collection muscles help your horse use his extension muscles properly, preventing injuries to joints, tendons, and ligaments). Balance your horse's muscle development by focusing on exercises that cause him to lift his back and stretch his topline, such as trotting over cavalettis or asking him to step his hindquarters underneath himself.

Another great exercise is to ask him to walk backward with his head down and his back rounded.

Horses in Self-Carriage

Regardless of whether you horse is a collection, extension, or balanced body type, it's important to make sure that he is always in "self-carriage" when you are riding him—otherwise he might damage his back. If you're not sure whether your horse is in self-carriage, have someone watch as you ride. As he walks, if his back foot steps forward at least even with his front hoof print, then he is walking in a balanced way. The more the back hoof print overreaches the front hoof print, the more the horse is moving off of his hind end. If his back feet are trailing behind his front hoof prints, make sure your legs are in contact with his sides and squeeze to encourage him to lift his back and step more under himself with his hind feet.

Horse not in self-carriage.   The same horse in self-carriage.

A Few Examples

All this terminology can be pretty confusing so I've included a couple of examples to help clarify the situation.

Marcus

Our first example is Marcus, a show jumper. Marcus is an Appendix Quarter Horse with a fairly long frame, powerful shoulders and haunches, and a well-developed top line. He can collect and extend with equal ease, and displays both speed and a self-supporting posture. Marcus has a balanced body type, and an ideal training program would include extension and collection work in equal quantities.

Musick

Musick, on the other hand, is a long tall Thoroughbred built for speed. His natural gaits are long and low, and he has a hard time collecting his body into a short frame. He also has a poorly developed top line. A balanced training program for Musick would include a lot of lateral work, backing, trotting over cavalettis, and alternately lengthening and shortening the stride.

In the real world, very few horses fit perfectly into one category or the other, but chances are your horse leans toward collection, extension, or balance. All things considered, your goal is to develop a training program that balances your horse's body type, the requirements of your riding discipline, and your horse's long-term physical health. I have found that variety in training is the true key for a well-developed horse. Plus, it's the spice of life!

Collection for Timed-Event Horses

Having examined the three body types and delved into various exercises for collection and extension, I want to go further by emphasizing the importance of developing collection in performance horses, especially timed-event horses. At first glance collection might seem like the last thing you would want for a timed event, but let's take a closer look. True collection can only occur when the horse is in self-carriage and the hind end is moving up under the body in response to cues from the rider's seat and legs. False collection occurs when the front end is compressed by pulling back on the reins. When in self-carriage the horse is able to collect and execute changes in speed or direction quickly and without losing his balance.

A horse conditioned only for speed will lose agility and be harder to control because he can't respond efficiently and quickly to the rider's aids. The perfect example is the jumper that fights his rider all the way to the jump and, when finally released, jumps flat and takes down a pole. This type of horse may actually be more talented than, but may often lose to, the smoother, more balanced jumper. In barrel events a horse who cannot collect will often run past the barrels or turn wide circles around them.

How to Train for Collection

- Ride on uneven terrain in all gaits so the horse learns how to carry himself and make adjustments as ground conditions change.

- Make changes of gait every few strides to help the horse pay attention and learn how to prepare himself for transitions. This is especially important for ex-racehorses who have to unlearn the habit of balancing on the reins and running faster. Don't overdo this exercise.

- Ride up and down the sides of hills. If possible incorporate turns in both directions.

- Lateral Work: For a horse to move forward and laterally (sideways) at the same time he must be able to balance himself in order to keep from falling. The leg-yield, shoulder-in, haunches-in, and the more advanced half-pass will help develop self-carriage.

- Work over poles or small jumps to encourage the horse to lower his head and lift his back.

- Make small circles, serpentines, and spirals. Horses must balance themselves to make tight turns so rather than working on straight lines, which can encourage a horse to lean on his forehand, ask him for frequent changes in direction starting with a large circle and spiraling into a smaller circle. Make sure you don't let the horse balance on the reins. Use your legs at the girth to keep the horse coming forward and up under himself.

Speed without balance is dangerous to both the horse and rider. An unbalanced horse cannot rate his speed and is more likely to injure himself if he tries to make an adjustment. Unbalanced horses who are ridden for any length of time will get sore because they have not developed the proper muscles to support themselves, much less a rider. Incorporating balance exercises into your strength and speed conditioning program will help your horse be a better athlete and lessen his chance of injury.

Chapter 13
Building & Maintaining Peak Energy
Through Natural Supplements

Performance Horse Health

Given horses with the same level of talent, trainers with equal amounts of dedication, and riders with unbeatable levels of competitiveness, winning on the performance circuit often boils down to the horse's ability to maintain vibrant health.

Building Peak Energy in the Performance Horse

Maintaining peak energy in performance horses is always a concern for performance horse owners, especially those who compete in speed events. To get the best performance from your horse with the least amount of damage to their bodies you should look at three areas. For muscles to perform at their best you must consider:

- Fuel Supply
- Oxygen Supply
- Mechanical Efficiency

Fuel Supply

Fuel can come from three sources: glucose in the blood from the breakdown of glycogen in the liver or muscle cells, lactate (which is recycled from the breakdown of glycogen), or fatty acids from the breakdown of triglycerides in fat cells.

High carbohydrate diets do raise the glycogen levels in muscles, which can be useful, but these diets can also contribute to metabolic problems in horses such as colic, laminitis, ulcers, or tying up. For this reason many knowledgeable horsemen have started feeding a diet balanced in fat and carbohydrates to provide for the energy needs of their horses. Fat is a good source of energy, and slows down the metabolism of carbohydrates.

Rice bran, ground flax seed, or vegetable oils are all good sources of fat for horses. These can be top dressed onto whole grains such as oats, corn, and/or barley. Sweet feeds that contain large amounts of molasses should be avoided because the rapid increase in blood sugar stresses the body and can eventually lead to insulin resistance. Also, horses on sweet feed diets often exhibit excess nervous energy that can make them difficult to handle and more likely to injure themselves. In my opinion giving sweet feed to horses is about as healthy as giving candy bars to children. It can be a nice treat but should not be a significant source of energy in a diet.

With the recent interest in high fat diets, many manufacturers have created feeds that contain fat. I do not generally like processed feeds because I'm never sure exactly what ingredients are being used. Plus, the processing destroys many nutrients, and larger amounts of preservatives, often chemical, are needed with processed high fat feeds.

Two exceptions are Purina's Equine Senior and Ultium, both of which seem to work well for many performance horses. In fact, they are perfect substitutes for horses who develop ulcers on full grain diets. For horses who work very hard it may be useful to feed some grain in addition to Equine Senior and Ultium. Although designed for older horses, Equine Senior provides working horses with a good balance of carbohydrates, fat, and fiber with less risk of digestive problems such as colic or ulcers. Ultium is a similar feed with a lower protein and higher fat content.

Oxygen Supply

A combination of healthy lungs and good circulation are needed to keep working muscles supplied with plenty of oxygen. Performance horses also need to have enough red blood cells to carry the oxygen. The combination of very heavy exercise, which can break down red blood cells, and chronic blood loss from intestinal ulcers can make many performance horses more susceptible to developing chronic anemia. While there are many synthetic iron tonics on the market, I have found the whole food blue-green algae to be one of the most effective blood tonics.

Healthy lungs are critical for good oxygen supply to the muscles. The performance horse's lungs are often compromised by the stale air in horse trailers and closed barns. Feeding probiotics on a regular basis will help thin the mucous in the lungs so it can be more easily moved out of the body along with any debris that the horse breathes in.

Mechanical Efficiency

Even the fittest horse cannot perform if his body mechanics are out of balance. Stiffness or lameness will cause the body to work inefficiently and use fuel and oxygen at an accelerated rate. Regular chiropractic or other bodywork will keep the performance horse working at his best.

Lack of adequate antioxidants can also slow down a top athlete. Free radicals are formed as a natural byproduct of exercise and, if not neutralized, they can lead to tissue damage, muscle stiffness, and joint problems. Natural antioxidants such as blue-green algae, wheat sprouts, or noni juice should be a regular part of the performance horse diet.

To sum things up, make sure you're offering your performance horse every chance to succeed:

- Feed a well-balanced diet to supply fuel for energy without causing metabolic problems.

- Develop a training program that builds oxygen uptake and carrying capacity in the blood.

- Avoid overtraining, which could cause injury or excess free radical formation.

Using Natural Supplements for Your Performance Horse

I once took my four-year-old mule, Jake, to a fairly intense training clinic where I had the opportunity to see the power of natural supplements at work. Here's what happened: When we joined the other 13 riders in the ring the first morning, Jake was a bit overwhelmed. He was pretty wound up with all the activity and just a step away from an out-of-mule-body experience. It occurred to me that I had not given him any Rescue Remedy (a vibrational flower essence remedy for stress) or taken any myself. I usually give us both Rescue Remedy when we face something new and challenging. I took Jake back to the trailer and we both took a dose. The rest of the morning went much better.

It was a long day and the heat index was well over 100 degrees. Jake gave his all and was a bit sore and grouchy at the end of the day. I took a little extra time to do a short Bowen session on him to help his muscles relax. In addition to his extra probiotics and algae at dinner, I also gave him an extra dose of noni juice to help with any inflammation from the extra work. The next morning Jake was bright and ready to go and did not need any Rescue Remedy, as he was very comfortable with his new surroundings.

I read an article in *Practical Horseman* about medicating performance horses and was dismayed to see that the supplements I had used at the clinic to help Jake would be considered illegal. The article specifically said,

> *"The United States Equestrian Federation's drugs and medication rules are clear: Anything that's given to a horse, in any way, with the intent to alter the horse's performance, be it through pain control or temperament adjustment, is not permitted. That means anything you give your horse— homeopathic, herbal, or otherwise—that's meant to calm him or make him more comfortable is illegal unless expressly permitted by the USEF."*

I feel we should draw a distinction between substances that help restore a horse to its natural physical, mental, and emotional state, and substances that actually increase a horse's performance beyond his normal abilities, have an altering effect on his brain function (i.e., tranquilization), or mask pain. Since this can be quite confusing, I'll give a couple of examples.

Consider the difference between the vibrational/energetic flower essence Rescue Remedy and the herb valerian. Both have calming effects. The difference is that valerian contains narcotic-like properties that can actually alter a horse's state beyond what is normal for him, while Rescue Remedy will only restore a horse to his normal state of calmness. Valerian can cause a horse that is usually not very calm to become calm or even sedated. On the other hand, Rescue Remedy would not have much of a calming effect on a horse like this because it would not alter what is "normal" for him. Rescue Remedy is effective in restoring a normally calm horse to his regular state under stressful conditions.

Another example is the difference between the homeopathic remedy Arnica (not the herbal form) and the herb devil's claw, both of which reduce symptoms of soreness or pain. Being another vibrational remedy with no chemical properties, Arnica cannot mask pain, but will help a horse recover from muscle soreness more quickly than he would without it. It will not, however, allow a horse to perform beyond his actual level of fitness. In contrast, devil's claw has some medicinal components that would act in the body like a non-steroidal anti-inflammatory drug, so *could* mask pain. When regulations allow for low levels of non-steroidal anti-inflammatory agents such as Bute or Banamine, devil's claw should be a perfectly acceptable substitute.

In these examples, we are making a distinction between nutritional supplements or homeopathic remedies and herbal supplements. Some herbs, such as valerian, kava kava, and devil's claw are medicinal and chemical in action. Even though they are natural substances and may not be harmful to the horse, using them to alter performance does violate the spirit of fair competition. On the other hand, vibrational/ energetic remedies and nutritional products that do not have chemical-like constituents cannot alter performance and instead allow a horse to be his best.

Homeopathic remedies and flower essences work on a vibrational plane and cannot mask pain or cause a horse to act in a certain way. Homeopathic remedies will never show up in tests because they are not physical substances. They also do not have side effects or harm the horse in any way.

Similarly, nutritional support from natural products such as probiotics, noni juice, or aloe vera will not alter a horse's performance but can help the horse recover more quickly and be more comfortable. Stress from showing will often cause the bacterial flora of the horse's digestive tract to change, and this can cause discomfort and make a horse nervous. Probiotics are a natural way to bring back the balance and help a horse feel better. Noni and aloe vera are considered herbs but they act in a nutritional rather than medicinal way by giving the horse extra enzymes and nutrients to recover quickly from stress. Blue-green algae is a concentrated nutrient which supports overall health so can give a horse extra energy and help him focus better at home or on the road.

The best way to be successful with your performance horse is to train him carefully, give him the best nutrition, condition him to be able to withstand the rigors of competition, and support him with natural products which do not mask pain or alter performance. I do not see how giving homeopathic remedies, flower essences, or nutritional products interferes with the spirit of the medication rules for shows and performances.

Chapter 14
On the Road

This section is dedicated to the performance riders and their horses who are constantly on the road, facing long hours in the rig, bad food, and lots of stress. Here are some ways to keep you and your horse in tip top shape during the show season:

- Preparing to Hit the Road
- Top 10 Ways Performance Horses Lose Their Edge
- How to Help Your Horse Avoid Burnout
- Consider Having a Horse Caddie

Preparing to Hit the Road

My experience in working with nationally ranked barrel racers tells me that we need to start preparing our horses for show season before we ever hit the road. Horses who are constantly on the road during show season need the best nutritional and holistic support possible in order to maintain their performance throughout the season. If you are thinking about showing this year, here's a quick checklist to help you prepare your horse:

- **Teeth:** Performance horses need their teeth checked at least twice a year to prevent colic, mouth pain, weight loss, and other health issues related to the teeth that could interfere with performance.

- **Digestion:** To support your horse's immune system and keep him calm, consider using digestive support such as probiotics, digestive enzymes, or the SUCCEED digestive conditioning product.

- **Joints:** Keep your horse's joints flexible and sound with joint support products and anti-inflammatories such as noni juice, CoQ10, vitamin C, or super oxide dismutase. Be sure and check show regulations on allowable products.

- **Immunity:** Since your horse will be exposed to other horses and possibly infectious diseases at shows, offer him extra immune support with beta glucan, probiotics, enzymes, and blue-green algae.

- ***Bodywork***: Hard training and showing can lead to sore muscles and spinal misalignments. Keep your horse fit and sound with regular chiropractic adjustments, acupuncture, equine touch, and other forms of bodywork.

Taking the time to prepare your horse before show season starts, and supporting him throughout the season, can pay many dividends as you head down the road.

Top Ten Ways Performance Horses Lose Their Edge

I have worked with several top competitors at the National Finals Rodeo (NFR), and I never cease to be amazed by how much care they give their horses. This high level of care, which keeps the horses sound for competitions all year long and for ten days straight at the NFR, takes real dedication and attention to detail.

Based on my observations, the competitors who take the most holistic approach to caring for their horses have the greatest chance of success. A successful competitor will typically have his or her horse's teeth checked twice a year by a competent dentist, and will often fly farriers, massage therapists, and chiropractors to out-of-town events to work on his or her horse as needed during competitions.

The best riders also carefully fit and maintain their tack, and use a variety of boots, magnetic blankets, ice boots, poultices, braces, and sweats to speed recovery from muscle soreness and minor injuries. The horse's nutrition is managed down to the last detail, starting with the highest quality feed and enhanced with supplements that support the immune system, digestion, and joints.

Finally, the best riders create and stringently follow custom-tailored conditioning programs and workouts for their horses, knowing that both horse and rider must be mentally and physically focused to succeed.

These riders have come to understand that their horses are much more likely to withstand the rigors of competition when they have a solid foundation of health, and they strive to develop a unique program that allows each horse to perform at his peak as often as possible.

While I have specifically mentioned rodeo horses in this section, the same principles apply to any performance horse. If you are actively campaigning a performance horse and you are not doing as well as you would like, you might be missing one or two pieces of the puzzle. Check out my list of the top ten ways you might be losing your edge below.

1. ***Showing an Unsuitable Horse:*** Before you check any of the other items below, first make sure that you have a horse that is suitable physically and mentally for the events in which you want to compete. A tall lanky Thoroughbred probably will not do well as a cutting horse, while a short, heavy Quarter Horse bred for cow work may not like jumping. And remember too that a two- or three-year-old horse is still a baby and may not be ready to handle a full training and work schedule.

2. ***Dental Needs:*** You communicate with your horse through your seat, hands, and voice. If your horse has any pain or discomfort in his mouth, you've just lost one channel of communication. Get your horse's teeth checked at least once a year, and more if you're competing at high levels.

3. ***Poor Quality Feed:*** "You get out of it what you put into it" and "You are what you eat" are sayings that definitely hold true when it comes to feeding your horse. Feeding poor quality or unsuitable feed will not take you far in the performance world. Determine what kind of feed is best for your horse and then get the best quality you can.

4. ***Tack That Doesn't Fit:*** Saddles, bits, and bridles that do not fit can cause discomfort, soreness, and frustration for your horse. If your horse isn't going as well as you like, try a variety of saddles, bits, bridles, and pads to see if that is the source of the problem. Some top competitors will try half a dozen bits and bridles before settling on the best choice for each horse.

5. ***Lack of Conditioning:*** Your horse will not perform well if he is over- or under-trained for the events in which you want to compete. Get expert help if necessary to create the perfect conditioning program for you and your horse.

6. ***Relying on Joint Injections:*** If you find yourself having to rely on frequent joint injections to keep your horse moving well, you might consider changing your horse's nutritional program. Frequent joint soreness indicates a need for support in the form of natural anti-inflammatories, antioxidants, and minerals.

Good sources of anti-inflammatories and antioxidants include coenzyme Q10, noni juice, and MSM. Blue-green algae is a good source of minerals, and glucosamine/chondroitin products work well specifically for joint support.

7. ***Drilling a Seasoned Horse:*** Overworking or over-drilling a seasoned performance horse can sour his attitude. If you have an experienced horse, keep the training to a minimum and make sure he has a variety of other activities in his life.

8. ***Overuse of Synthetic Vitamins and Minerals:*** Adding too many non-natural sources of vitamins or minerals to your horse's diet can put a lot of stress on his liver and kidneys, plus he may stop eating since these supplements often don't taste good. As much as possible, design a customized program for your horse based on supplements in natural, whole-food form.

9. ***Too Little Variety:*** Remember that horses are herd animals that are meant to wander over acres and acres of land, grazing as they go. Allow your horse plenty of pasture time with his buddies, and create alternative conditioning options in different disciplines. For instance, you might trail ride or work cows on a jumper just to offer a change of scenery.

10. ***Using Drugs Rather than Solid Nutrition:*** If you have to give your horse non-steroidal anti-inflammatory drugs every time you work him because he gets sore, you might need to upgrade his nutritional program. A well-conditioned horse who gets solid nutrition will not get sore every time he is worked. Substitute natural antioxidants for non-steroidal anti-inflammatory drugs to combat normal muscle soreness from heavy training or competition.

How to Help Your Horse Avoid Burnout
We've all seen performance horses who get burned out from too much work and too little support. They go off their feed, have dull hair coats, act depressed, have bad attitudes, or just stop performing well. It's a sad situation because burnout can be easily avoided with sound management and proper nutrition.

What Causes Burnout?

Burnout is the result of an imbalance in the horse's nervous system. Every horse's nervous system has two components: sympathetic and parasympathetic. In brief, the sympathetic nervous system is the "fight or flight" mechanism while the parasympathetic is the rest and relaxation portion.

When your horse is working or training, he is using the sympathetic nervous system, and when he is turned out in pasture or eating, he is using the parasympathetic. For optimum health your horse needs a balance between the two. Too much time in the parasympathetic leads to a fat unconditioned horse, while too much time in the sympathetic leads to burnout.

Horses who have already reached burnout may or may not be able to recover fully. If the adrenal glands (the glands in the sympathetic nervous system that produce the fight or fight hormones) are not too damaged, the horse may recover with six or more months of rest supported by a strong nutritional program that will help them heal. Horses who have been in burnout for too long may never recover. These horses will need special care and nutritional supplementation for the rest of their lives. They may be able to work sporadically, but will then require lengthy recovery periods.

How to Prevent Burnout

There are four main actions steps that you can take to help your horse avoid burnout:

1. **Feed Less:** On rest days, feed your horse fewer calories and supplements and more hay. Too many calories produce excess energy, preventing your horse from resting (more on feeding in the guidelines below).

2. **Offer Social and Rest Time:** Give your horse plenty of down time between heavy workouts. Turn him out, preferably with other horses, so he can socialize, roll, put his head down, switch flies, and generally act like a horse. Horses, like all social animals, need companionship and relaxation.

3. **Keep Him Pain Free:** Horses in pain cannot rest and relax, even when they are turned out. Use chiropractic, acupuncture,

and bodywork to keep your horse's nervous system, connective tissues, and muscles in top physical condition. Offer nutritional support like noni juice for muscle soreness, and homeopathic remedies like Arnica after heavy workouts.

4. ***Make Life Interesting:***
Nothing burns a horse out faster than seeing the same scenery over and over again. Instead of drilling your horse in the same discipline all the time, keep his life varied with activities in other disciplines. If you have a dressage horse, try trail riding, working cattle, or jumping to keep life interesting. Even hauling your horse down the road to a friend's house can be stimulating.

Keep life interesting!

Feeding to Prevent Burnout

One of the most ignored factors in preventing burnout is nutrition. If you want your horse to be able to rest and relax, you have to give him fuel that is useful to the parasympathetic, or resting, part of the nervous system. That usually means less grain, fewer high energy supplements, and more hay. Grain and supplements are high-powered fuels that can overexcite your horse's nervous system, keeping him in a sympathetic rather than parasympathetic nervous system mode. Eating hay, on the other hand, doesn't produce a lot of energy and actually relaxes your horse.

For instance, on work days it is typical for a performance horse to need more feed and supplements to fuel his energy output, but on a rest day, I would cut everything in half and offer more free choice hay. For a light work or travel day, I would give the horse two-thirds of his heavy work regimen plus plenty of hay.

One reason you want to cut back the amount of grain and supplements you feed on a rest day is so that your horse will want to eat more hay, which is a very relaxing activity. Horses are designed to walk and eat 23 hours a day, so eating hay is one of the best activities you can offer your horse to prevent burnout.

On the flip side of the coin, feeding more grain (especially after work to rebuild glycogen stores) and less hay on heavy training days works well since you don't really want your horse carrying a heavy load of hay around in his guts as he works. That being said, you still want to offer him enough hay to prevent ulcers and gut pain.

What To Do If Your Horse Is On the Edge

If you suspect that your horse might be close to burning out, consider giving him some time off to let his mind and body, especially his adrenal glands, recover. Equilite GinZing is my favorite product for supporting the adrenals. During the recovery time it is still important to keep your horse on a good nutritional program, but only maintenance levels of feed and supplements are needed.

Consider Having a Horse Caddie

Whenever I return from a behind-the-scenes tour of the barrel racing world I feel compelled to address the holistic care of the high-performance rider. What I see on the circuit over and over is that riders devote so much of their attention to their horse's care that they neglect themselves. The result? Burnout and fatigue, which can lead to mistakes and the inability to cope—all of which ultimately leads to less-than-perfect care for their horse!

So how can we take care of ourselves holistically while on the road? I've noticed that some of the best riders on the circuit have the equivalent of a golf caddie—a support person who helps them in many ways. To give you a better idea of the support person's role, I did a little research on what golf caddies do. Here's what the Professional Caddies Association says about their job:

> *"Today, the role of the tour caddie has evolved into that of the player's partner and right hand. As an important part of the team, caddies can help a golfer in many ways. They help set the overall game plan, and plan of attack to each hole. They help manage the player's game, provide important knowledge of exact distances to various golf course targets and obstacles, give psychological support and steady a player through the myriad of thoughts that can play in a golfer's mind and create tension."*

Top performance riders need the same kind of support and guidance. Here's what your horse caddie should do for you (or what you should do for yourself if you don't yet have a caddie):

- Ensure that you get plenty of sleep.

- Provide plenty of pure water. (Note: beer and soft drinks are not pure water and actually dehydrate you!)

- Provide healthy food. (Translation: not food from the concession stand.)

- Offer nutritional supplements for when you are forced to eat from the concession stand.

- Help you drive. (Many riders equate driving with rest but it's not because you have to stay alert—you need actual down time so you can focus your thoughts and work on your game plan, or just plain rest!)

- Keep your living area tidy and your clothes clean so you feel rested, peaceful, and prepared.

A tidy tackroom makes life on the road easier.

If you are the horse caddie, here are some things to keep in mind:

1. ***Horse Care:*** Most riders like to tend to their horse's care themselves, but you can step in if needed. You should not only know how to feed the horse when asked to, but should also assume responsibility for keeping plenty of vet supplies, feed, supplements, and support wraps on hand. Finally, keep tack clean, in good repair, and well organized.

2. ***Routine:*** Stay aware of your rider's routine for saddling and warm-up, and know what equipment they might use under different conditions.

3. ***Support:*** Remember that support comes in many forms. There will be a lot of fetching and carrying, but the moral support you'll be providing is even more important. I feel that this quote about the role of the golf caddie (again from the Professional Caddies Association) is a great model for horse caddies:

   "They employed knowledge of wind, ground, distance, and of how conditions affect what route to take. They quickly learned the way you

hit the ball...and they would take you around the golf course like a guide instead of some sort of packhorse."

Conclusion

Whether you're the horse, the rider, or the caddie, the most important aspect of holistic care is that it is *"whole*-istic." It is about the approach, not the technique. That means that all members of the team—humans and horses—are treated as individuals with unique needs and are cared for, supported, and nurtured.

Appendix
Resources, Products, & Supplies

Locating a Holistic Practitioner

Academy of Veterinary Homeopathy
(866) 652-1590
www.theavh.org

American Academy of Veterinary Acupuncture
(860) 635-6300
www.aava.org

American Holistic Veterinary Medical Association
(410) 569-0795
www.ahvma.org

American Veterinary Chiropractic Association
(918) 784-2231
www.animalchiropractic.org

Chi Institute of Chinese Medicine
(800) 891-1986
www.tcvm.com

International Veterinary Acupuncture Society
(970) 266-0666
www.ivas.org

Veterinary Botanical Medicine Association
www.vbma.org

Homeopathic Remedies

Washington Homeopathic
(800) 336-1695
www.homeopathyworks.com

Products

AVON Skin So Soft
AVON Products, Inc.
1-800-FOR-AVON
www.avon.com

Blue-Green Algae Products by Cell Tech
1-800-800-1300
www.celltech.com
Dr. Ward's ID#304542
    Animal Matrix for Horses
    Beta Glucan (Immusun)
    Blue-Green Algae ("Simply SBGA")
    Coenzyme Q10
    Enzymes
    Omega Form of Blue-Green Algae
    Regular Essentials
    Super Sprouts & Algae (Super Oxide Dismutase)

Calf Manna
Manna Pro
1-800-690-9908
www.mannapro.com

CoEnzymeQ10
Thorne
1-800-228-1966
www.thorne.com
Nutramax
1-800-924-5187
www.nutramaxlabs.com

Colostrum Products (Transfer Factors)
www.4life.com

Draw Solution
Advanced Biological Concepts
1-800-373-5971
www.a-b-c-plus.com

Electrolytes
Ions and Ride Rite
Advanced Biological Concepts
1-800-373-5971
www.a-b-c-plus.com

Electrolytes (Acculytes)
Vita Flex
1-800-848-2359
www.vitaflex.com

Farrier's Formula
Life Data Labs., Inc.
(256) 370-7555
www.lifedatalabs.com

Fastrack
Conklin
1-800-756-2475
Dr. Ward's ID#34643940

Formula 11
Circle Star Farms
www.circlestarfarms.com

Free Choice Minerals
Advanced Biological Concepts
1-800-373-5971
www.a-b-c-plus.com

Free Choice Minerals
SweetPro
1-800-327-9222
www.equipride.biz

GinZing
Equilite
1-800-942-LITE
www.equilite.com

Hypericum, Calendula or Arnica Tinctures
Washington Homeopathic
1-800-336-1695
www.homeopathyworks.com

Natural Balance Pads
www.hopeforsoundness.com

N.O.M.S
Advanced Biological Concepts
1-800-373-5971
www.a-b-c-plus.com

Noni Juice (Equine Essentials)
Tahitian Noni
1-800-445-2969
www.tahitiannoni.com
Dr. Ward's ID#1360218
or www.holistichorsekeeping.com

Oculotrophin
Standard Process
1-800-848-5061
www.standardprocess.com

Rescue Remedy
Washington Homeopathic
1-800-336-1695
www.homeopathyworks.com

Sore No More
Equilite
1-800-942-LITE
www.equilite.com

SUCCEED
www.holistichorsekeeping.com

Tea Tree Oil
Frontier Herbs
1-800-669-3275
www.frontiercoop.com

Yucca/Devil's Claw
Equilite
1-800-942-LITE
www.equilite.com

Vitamin C (Citrus C/Q)
Equilite
1-800-942-LITE
www.equilite.com

Laboratories
Analysis of Parasites in Blood
APC Equine Research Bio-Lab
(765) 659-5209
www.indianahorserescue.com

Bloodworm Testing: Igt for Migrating Strongyles
Texas Veterinary Medical Diagnostic Lab
(979) 845-3414

Titers
Texas Veterinary Medical Diagnostic Lab
(979) 845-3414
Kansas State University Diagnostic Laboratory (Rabies)
(785) 532-5650

Additional Reading

Equine Acupressure: A Working Manual, Nancy Zidonis, Amy Snow, Marie Soderberg

Feeding and Care of the Horse, Lon D. Lewis

Groundwork, Buck Brannaman

Healing with Whole Foods, Paul Pitchford

Horse Owner's Guide to Natural Hoof Care, Jaime Jackson

Making Natural Hoof Care Work for You, Pete Ramey

Nutritional Herbology, Mark Pedersen

Pocket Manual of Homeopathic Materia Medica, William Boericke, MD

Simpify Your Riding: Step-by-Step Techniques to Improve Your Riding Skills, Wendy Murdoch

The Horse's Pain-Free Back and Saddle-Fit Book, Joyce Harman, DVM, MRCVS

Ebooks

Horse Types and Temperaments: The Six Temperaments Ebook, by Madalyn Ward, DVM, www.holistichorsekeeping.com

Horse Types and Temperaments: The Five Types Ebook, by Madalyn Ward, DVM, www.holistichorsekeeping.com

Laminitis Treatment: A Natural Medicine Perspective Ebook, by Joyce Harman, DVM, MRCVS, and Madalyn Ward, DVM, www.holistichorsekeeping.com

Index

A

abscess(es) 37, 60, 72, 80, 81, 83, 87
acidophilus 106
aconite 74, 83, 84, 86, 87
acupressure 11, 47, 48
acupuncture 3, 4, 6, 8, 10, 11, 12, 13, 17, 28
Adamson, Cecilia 38
Adequan 44, 45
adhesions 16, 48
adjustments 14, 16, 17, 116, 125, 132
adjuvants 52, 62
alfalfa 25, 28, 42, 77, 78, 92
allergies 6, 25, 49, 91, 100, 101
amino acids 5, 22, 32
anemia 58, 127
anhydrosis 88, 99, 100
antacids 100, 101
anti-inflammatory, anti-inflammatories 24, 45, 46, 74, 76, 79, 81, 98, 101, 106, 111, 112, 129, 131, 133, 134
antibiotics 4, 23, 37, 72, 81, 89, 90, 96, 101, 107
antibody 26, 51, 52, 101, 102
antibody titers 58
antigen 26, 52, 61, 62, 98, 102
antigens/antibody complexes 26, 52, 101, 102
antihistamines 107
antioxidants 25, 26, 41, 42, 43, 44, 45, 46, 72, 74, 89, 90, 91, 103, 106, 110, 128, 133, 134
antispasmodic herbs 106
Apis 74, 83, 84
aqua puncture 11
Arnica 37, 74, 79, 80, 83, 84, 129, 136
Arsenicum 83, 84, 85
arthritis 2, 45
ascarids 63, 65, 66, 90
avermectins 66
Azium 95

B

B-Complex vitamins 23
bacteria 4, 5, 11, 23, 24, 25, 29, 33, 34, 56, 58, 61, 72, 76, 99, 101, 103, 105, 108
Banamine 45, 76, 79, 129
barefoot 36, 38, 39, 103
barley 20, 28, 93, 103, 126
beet pulp 28, 30
Belladonna 74, 83, 87
Bennett, Carol 48
benzimidazoles 66
beta carotene 22, 42, 97, 99
Betadine 38, 39
beta glucan 72, 81, 90, 106, 131
bioflavonoids 109
biotin 25, 33
blindness 97, 98
blood worms 65
blue-green algae 24, 25, 26, 27, 28, 32, 33, 38, 40, 42, 43, 44, 45, 72, 89, 90, 92, 94, 97, 99, 100, 103, 107, 110, 112, 127, 128, 131, 130, 134
body type 113, 120, 121, 122, 123, 124
Bowen 43, 48, 49, 128
Bowker, Robert M. (VMD and Ph.D.) 35
bran 20, 21, 27, 28, 72, 76, 77, 79, 93, 126
Brannaman, Buck 114
bronchoalveolar lavage (BAL) 90, 108
bronchodialators 90, 107
bruise, bruises, bruising 31, 33, 36, 37, 80, 108
burnout 131, 134, 135, 136, 137
Bute 2, 45, 79, 129

C

calendula 83, 85, 94, 98
Calf Manna 93
capillary, capillaries 71, 72, 108, 109
carbohydrates 29, 30, 42, 103, 126, 127
cartilage(s) 2, 3, 24, 31, 34, 35, 41, 43, 44, 45, 46
cells 13, 14, 22, 26, 27, 31, 96, 101, 106, 108, 126, 127

Cell Tech 28, 74, 99, 103, 107, 112
Chamomile, Chamomilla 76, 78, 83, 85, 86
chelated minerals 21
chiropractic, chiropractor 8, 13, 14, 15, 17, 28, 46, 47, 89, 95, 128, 132, 135
chlorhexidine disinfectants 96
chlorophyll 22, 25, 89, 99
cholesterol 20
chondroitin sulphate 44, 45, 46
Chronic Obstructive Pulmonary Disease (COPD) 88, 90, 102
circulation 39, 40, 49, 73, 80, 88, 89, 96, 103, 127
Citrus C/Q 106
climate(s) 30, 33, 34, 63, 64, 93, 99
coenzyme Q10 42, 44, 45, 74, 103, 134
Colchicum 78, 83, 85
cold laser 11
colds 66, 86, 88, 89, 90
cold water 79, 100
colic 13, 24, 50, 53, 58, 59, 63, 65, 75, 76, 77, 78, 85, 86, 102, 126, 127, 131
collection 116, 120, 121, 122, 123, 124
colon 75, 77
colostrum 72, 81, 90
Conception Vessel 10
connective tissues 22, 40, 46, 136
constipation 12
constitutional 25, 60, 91, 99
CoQ10 22, 23, 26, 103, 131
corticosteroids 3, 94, 95, 107
cough(ing) 4, 5, 6, 12, 56, 72, 90, 91, 100, 105
cramping 75, 76, 85
cranio-sacral 16, 17
culicoides 94, 97
Cushing's disease 20, 103
cutaneous onchocerciasis 97
cyst 84

D
damp 11, 59, 67, 92, 93, 95, 96, 99

F

Farrier's Formula 32
Fastrack 33
fat horse(s) 26, 27
feet 32, 33, 34, 35, 36, 37, 38, 73, 74, 75, 77, 81, 117, 118, 119, 123
fever 4, 5, 6, 12, 52, 53, 56, 58, 72, 84, 102
flower essences 130
flu 50, 52, 53, 56, 61, 62, 71
Flu Avert 62
Fort Dodge 55
free choice 23, 100, 111, 112, 136
free radicals 18, 128
frog 31, 34, 35, 36, 38, 39, 40, 73, 80, 103
fructan(s) 29, 30
fungal, fungus 21, 34, 38, 92, 95, 96, 97, 106
Furacin 95

G

gas colic 77, 78, 85
gastrointestinal tract 23
gelding scars 16
gentling 114, 117
GinZing 137
glucosamine 24, 43, 44, 45, 46, 134
glucosamine/chondroitin 134
gnats 94, 97
Governing Vessel 10
grain(s) 18, 19, 20, 21, 24, 27, 28, 32, 33, 36, 42, 73, 78, 79, 80, 86, 100, 112, 126, 127, 136, 137
grass 19, 23, 24, 25, 28, 29, 30, 42, 74, 76, 77, 78, 89, 103, 104, 111
graze, grazing 28, 29, 63, 64, 68, 77, 111, 134
groundwork 48, 113, 114, 117, 118, 120
gut(s) 26, 61, 64, 66, 75, 76, 84, 88, 92, 100, 101, 102, 137

H

habronemiasis 95
Hahnemann, Samuel 8, 9, 82
hair, hair coat 4, 33, 50, 51, 59, 63, 67, 87, 92, 93, 94, 95, 96, 97, 134
head injuries 84

intestines 20, 23, 33, 65
itch, itchiness, itching 26, 92, 93, 94, 95, 97

J
Jackson, Jaime 103
jaw joint 68
joint(s) 2, 3, 12, 14, 16, 24, 27, 35, 41, 42, 43, 44, 45, 46, 47, 68, 84, 85, 102, 122, 128, 131, 132, 133, 134

K
kidney(s) 10, 21, 26, 89, 91, 134
Kopertox 33

L
lactic acid 23
lameness 11, 31, 35, 41, 49, 59, 80, 100, 127
laminar attachments 30
laminitic, laminitis 13, 23, 28, 27, 29, 30, 50, 53, 58, 72, 73, 74, 83, 88, 87, 102, 103, 104, 126
larvae 63, 64, 65, 66, 67, 93, 94, 95
Lasix 108, 109, 110
leaky gut syndrome 26, 88, 92, 100, 101, 102
Lite Salt 76
liver 3, 5, 6, 25, 66, 91, 101, 102, 126, 134
lobelia 106
lung(s) 6, 16, 66, 89, 90, 91, 106, 107, 108, 109, 127
lymph 58, 61, 88

M
macrophages 106
marshmallow 106
massage 47, 132
medicine, medication(s) 1, 2, 4, 5, 6, 7, 8, 9, 10, 11, 12, 25, 40, 46, 47, 72, 76, 78, 80, 82, 89, 96, 97, 98, 99, 101, 129, 130
melanomas 53
meningeal tension 14
Merial 55
meridian(s) 10, 11, 47, 49
metabolic, metabolism 18, 21, 23, 102, 103, 126, 128

rhinopneumonitis 50, 51, 59, 62
rice bran 28, 93, 126
ringworm 95, 96

S
sacrum 16
saddle(s), saddling 27, 48, 111, 114, 115, 119, 133, 138
salt(s) 37, 72, 80, 81, 92, 93 94
sarcoids 51, 87
scar(s), scarring 12, 16, 60, 66, 80
self-carriage 123, 124, 125
shock 31, 35, 71, 84
shoe(ing) 5, 35, 36, 37, 39, 91, 103
Silicea 59, 60, 81, 83, 87
skin 3, 26, 33, 34, 49, 51, 59, 60, 61, 75, 79, 80, 86, 87, 91, 92, 93, 94, 95, 96, 97, 99, 100, 101, 102
Soderberg, Marie 47
sole(s) 31, 33, 35, 36, 80, 103
sores 94, 95
spleen 10, 20, 92
spleen/pancreas 92
stiffness 12, 25, 46, 85, 100, 128
stomach 20, 26, 28, 67, 76, 77, 78, 95, 111
stomach acid 111
stone bruises 36, 80
strangles 6, 52, 53, 58
streptococcus 5, 6, 58
stress 5, 6, 14, 18, 23, 24, 27, 29, 46, 57, 72, 79, 85, 89, 100, 111, 112, 113, 128, 130, 131, 134
Strongid/StrongidC 64, 65, 66
strongyles 63, 64, 65, 66
SUCCEED 112, 131
sulphur 22, 32, 42, 44, 45, 46, 81, 83, 87
sweat, sweating 77, 96, 99, 100
sweet itch 94
swelling 14, 37, 47, 48, 58, 74, 79, 80, 84, 88, 89, 97

T
tail(s) 6, 16, 30, 67, 86, 94, 97

tapeworm(s) 63, 66, 67
teeth, tooth 21, 68, 69, 70, 79, 86, 131, 132, 133
Tellington TTouch 48
Tellington-Jones, Linda 48
temperament 129
tendon(s) 25, 27, 59, 102, 122
tension 14, 15, 16, 17, 48, 120, 137
tetanus 37, 50, 51, 55, 56, 59, 60, 61, 86
therapy, therapeutic 1, 3, 25, 26, 47, 91, 96
thin horse 27
thirst 84, 86
thrush 38, 39, 92
Thuja 59, 83, 87
thymus 61
tincture(s) 80, 83, 84, 86, 98
titer(s) 51, 55, 58, 98
TMJ *(see jaw joint)*
toxic, toxicity 4, 9, 25, 33, 52, 62, 65, 66, 84, 85, 91, 97, 108
toxins 15, 18, 29, 47, 49, 62, 88, 89, 96, 101, 102, 103
toxoid 37, 55, 56, 62
Traditional Chinese Medicine (TCM) 5, 11, 25, 47, 99
Trichophyton 95

U
ulcer(s) 20, 26, 28, 46, 98, 100, 110, 111, 112, 126, 127, 137
United States Equestrian Federation (USEF) 129
urine, urination 20, 32
urticaria 26, 102
uveitis 88, 97, 98

V
vaccinate, vaccination(s) 34, 50, 51, 52, 53, 54, 56, 57, 58, 59, 60, 61,
62, 87, 89, 91, 95, 99, 100, 101, 104, 107, 110
vaccinosis 51
valerian 129, 130
vertebrae 14, 15, 16
vibrational 48, 128, 129, 130
virus 4, 55, 56, 57, 58, 62, 105